The Open University

M208 Pure Mathematics

I1

Real functions and graphs

This publication forms part of an Open University course. Details of this and other Open University courses can be obtained from the Student Registration and Enquiry Service, The Open University, PO Box 197, Milton Keynes, MK7 6BJ, United Kingdom: tel. +44 (0)870 300 6090, e-mail general-enquiries@open.ac.uk

Alternatively, you may visit the Open University website at http://www.open.ac.uk where you can learn more about the wide range of courses and packs offered at all levels by The Open University.

To purchase a selection of Open University course materials, visit http://www.ouw.co.uk, or contact Open University Worldwide, Michael Young Building, Walton Hall, Milton Keynes, MK7 6AA, United Kingdom, for a brochure: tel. +44 (0)1908 858793, fax +44 (0)1908 858787, e-mail ouw-customer-services@open.ac.uk

The Open University, Walton Hall, Milton Keynes, MK7 6AA.

First published 2006. Reprinted with amendments 2007.

Edited, designed and typeset by The Open University, using the Open University TEX System.

Printed and bound in the United Kingdom by Hobbs the Printers Limited, Brunel Road, Totton, Hampshire SO40 3WX.

ISBN 0 7492 6915 4

1.2

Contents

Introduction to the block

M208 covers a wide range of pure mathematics; and each block apart from this one concentrates on one topic. This block is different because it discusses some of the underlying concepts which will reappear in most of the other blocks.

Since this is a Level 2 course, we are expecting all students to have studied mathematics to approximately Level 1 standard, though not necessarily with the Open University. This block gives you the chance to brush up, or meet for the first time, some Level 1 concepts and to get used to the notation which we use. If you are new to the Open University, it also gives you a chance to get used to the supported open learning method of study.

In Unit I1 we concentrate on the concept of a *real function*, and on how to draw the graph of such a function. We introduce a strategy for doing so. This gives us the opportunity to remind you of the graphs of various common functions, to introduce a wide range of functions, including *trigonometric* and *hyperbolic functions*, and to look at their properties. We finish by looking at some curves which are not necessarily the graphs of functions, but which are described in terms of a single parameter. These include circles, parabolas, hyperbolas and ellipses, known collectively as *conics*.

Unit I2 concentrates on mathematical language. We discuss the mathematical idea of a *set* (usually of numbers or of points in the plane), and look at the ideas of two sets being equal and of one being a subset of the other. We also look at ways of combining sets. We then return to the idea of a function, introduced in Unit I1, and show how to compose functions and how to find the inverse of a function. Finally we turn to the important subject of mathematical proof, and show how to use different methods of proof, as well as disproving a statement by finding a counter-example.

Unit I3 looks at number systems and their properties. We first consider *real numbers*, and subsets of real numbers, such as natural numbers, integers and rational numbers. We then introduce *complex numbers*, investigate their properties and uses, and discuss some functions of complex numbers. We go on to look at *modular arithmetic*, and finally discuss *equivalence relations* and the idea of a *partition* of a set.

Introduction

A fundamental concept in mathematics is that of a *function*.

Consider, for example, the function f defined by

$$f(x) = 2x^2 - 1, \quad \text{where } 0 \le x \le 1.$$

This is an example of a *real function*, because it associates with a given real number x the real number $2x^2 - 1$: it maps real numbers to real numbers.

One way of picturing this function is the following. First, draw up a table of values, listing in the first row several values of x, and in the second row the corresponding values of $f(x)$; for example, $f(0.8) = 2(0.8)^2 - 1 = 0.28$.

x	0	0.1	0.2	0.3	0.4	0.5	0.6	0.7	0.8	0.9	1
$f(x)$	−1	−0.98	−0.92	−0.82	−0.68	−0.5	−0.28	−0.02	0.28	0.62	1

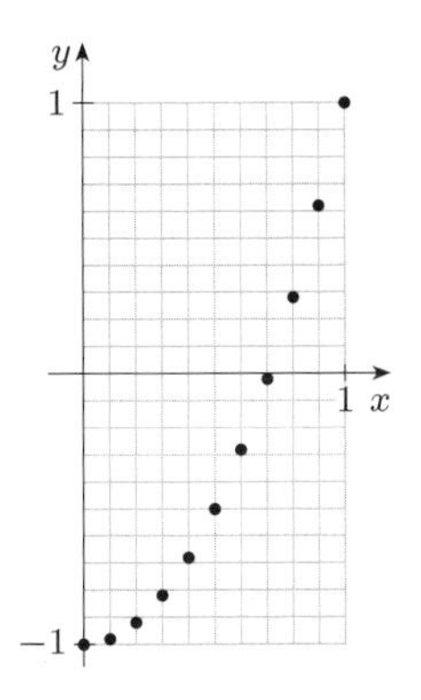

Each column in the table is essentially an ordered pair of the form $(x, f(x))$, which can be plotted as a unique point in the plane. We refer to the set of all such points as the *graph* of f.

Of course, it is not possible to plot all the points of the graph for a function like f, which is defined for infinitely many values of x. Fortunately, for many graphs plotting a few points provides a good idea of what the graph looks like. For any so-called 'well-behaved' function, these points can be joined up by a smooth curve—and extended if necessary—to complete the picture.

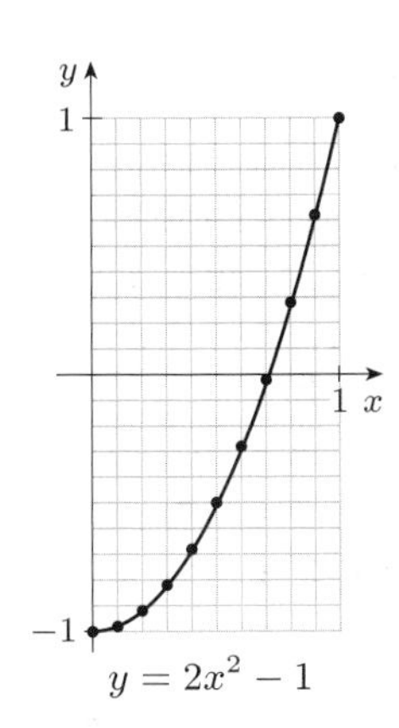

$y = 2x^2 - 1$

No doubt you are already familiar with this method of drawing a graph. However, it is not always the most efficient method to use when knowledge about the key features of the graph is all that is wanted. For the purposes of this course, that is all that is usually required.

Many problems are best studied by working with real functions, and the properties of real functions are often revealed most clearly by their graphs. Learning to sketch such graphs is therefore a useful skill, even though computer packages can now perform the task. Computers can plot many more points than can be plotted by hand, but simply 'joining up the dots' can sometimes give a misleading picture, so an understanding of how such graphs may be obtained remains important. The object of this unit is to review the various techniques for sketching graphs that you may have met in your previous studies, and to extend these methods.

If you have studied previous courses with the Open University, you may have used a graphics calculator or computer package to draw graphs.

In Section 1 we formally define *real functions* and describe how they may arise when we try to solve equations. We remind you of some basic real functions and their graphs, and describe how some of the properties of these functions are featured in their graphs.

In Section 2 we describe how the graphs of polynomial and rational functions may be sketched by analysing their behaviour—for example, by using techniques of calculus. We assume that you are familiar with basic calculus and that its use is valid. In particular, we assume that the graphs of the functions under consideration consist of smooth curves.

The validity of this assumption will be investigated in the analysis blocks.

In Section 3 we consider how to sketch the graphs of more complicated functions, sometimes involving trigonometric functions. We look at graphs which are sums, quotients and composites of different functions, and at those which are defined by a different rule for different values of x.

In Section 4 we introduce the *hyperbolic functions* sinh, cosh and tanh, which are constructed from exponential functions. These hyperbolic functions share some of the properties of the trigonometric functions but, as you will see, their graphs are very different.

In Section 5 we show how functions may be used to sketch curves in the plane, even when these curves are not necessarily the graphs of functions.

Study guide

Throughout this unit, we assume that you are familiar with basic calculus, and are able to manipulate simple inequalities.

Inequalities are discussed in Analysis Block A, and differentiation is studied in Analysis Block B.

Sections 1–5 should be studied in the natural order.

Section 1 contains an audio section in which we revise the properties of some familiar graphs, and introduce some concepts which form the basis of the graph-sketching strategy given in Section 2. Do not worry if you do not fully understand all the details at this stage, but concentrate on the main ideas. This audio section is important, but rather long, so we suggest that you take a break in the middle.

Section 2 is quite long and contains a number of important ideas and a useful strategy; it should be worked through carefully.

Sections 3, 4 and 5 are shorter than the previous two sections.

This unit contains many exercises—more than you could reasonably do during your study of the unit. Concentrate on attempting the exercises that deal with the techniques you find most difficult, leaving the remaining ones, and those in the 'Further exercises', for revision later. If you do not have time to do some of the exercises, it is worth looking at their solutions to check that you can follow them.

1 Real functions

After working through this section, you should be able to:

(a) understand the definition of a *real function*;

(b) use the notation for *intervals* of the real line;

(c) recognise and use the graphs of the basic functions described in the audio section;

(d) understand the effect on a graph of *translations*, *scalings*, *rotations* and *reflections*;

(e) understand how the shape of a graph of a function features properties of the function such as *increasing*, *decreasing*, *even* and *odd*.

1.1 What is a real function?

We begin by defining what we mean by a real function. We saw an example of such a function in the Introduction, where we discussed the function f defined by

$$f(x) = 2x^2 - 1, \quad \text{where } 0 \leq x \leq 1.$$

To each real number x in the range $0 \le x \le 1$ the above rule associates the unique real number $f(x)$.

The concept of a real function involves not just a rule, but also two associated sets of real numbers. The set of all real numbers is denoted by $\mathbb{R}$, and this set can be pictured as a number-line, often called the **real line**. We use the following definition.

We study the structure of $\mathbb{R}$ in Unit I3 and in Analysis Block A.

Definitions A **real function** f is defined by specifying

- a set of real numbers A, called the **domain** of f;
- a set of real numbers B, called the **codomain** of f;
- a **rule** that associates with each real number x in the set A a unique real number $f(x)$ in the set B.

The number $f(x)$ is the **image of x under f** or the **value of f at x**.

The definition does not require *every* number in B to be the image of a number in A (though it *does* require every number in A to have an image in B).

Usually we refer to a real function f simply as a 'function' unless there is a reason to emphasise that f is a real function.

There are several ways to specify a particular function. Take, for example, the function with domain and codomain $\mathbb{R}$ and rule $f(x) = x^2$. In this course we choose to write this function as

$$\begin{aligned} f: \mathbb{R} &\longrightarrow \mathbb{R} \\ x &\longmapsto x^2. \end{aligned}$$

The first arrow is unbarred to signify a mapping from the domain $\mathbb{R}$ to the codomain $\mathbb{R}$. The second arrow is barred, to show that the *particular* real number x maps to the *particular* real number x^2. Each arrow is read as 'maps to'.

If it is clear from the context that we are dealing with real functions, we shall write such a function simply as

$$f(x) = x^2 \quad \text{or} \quad x \longmapsto x^2.$$

To avoid uncertainty, we adopt the following convention.

Convention When a real function is specified *only by a rule*, it is to be understood that the domain of the function is the set of all real numbers for which the rule is applicable, and the codomain of the function is $\mathbb{R}$.

For example, the function

$$f(x) = 1/\sqrt{4 - x^2}$$

does not have domain $\mathbb{R}$, because the square root is a real number only when $4 - x^2 \ge 0$; that is, when $x^2 \le 4$. This is the case when x satisfies the inequalities $-2 \le x \le 2$, and for no other values of x. However, we cannot divide by 0, so we must exclude the values -2 and 2 from the domain. Thus the domain of f can be described as

the set of x belonging to $\mathbb{R}$ such that $-2 < x < 2$,

or

the set of all real numbers strictly between -2 and 2.

We introduce a mathematical notation for sets like this in Unit I2.

Exercise 1.1 For each of the following rules, determine the domain of the corresponding real function f.

(a) $x \longmapsto \dfrac{1}{1-x^2}$ (b) $x \longmapsto 4x^3 - 3x^2 - 6x + 4$

(c) $x \longmapsto \dfrac{x^2-5x+4}{x^2+5x+4}$ (d) $x \longmapsto \dfrac{1}{\sqrt{1-x^2}}$

As we have seen, many of the sets that arise as domains of functions are of the form $a < x < b$, extending along the real line from one number a to another number b. Each of the endpoints a and b may be either included or excluded. Such sets are called **intervals** of the real line, and they occur so frequently that we use special notation for them. For example,

We use $a < x < b$ as shorthand for 'the set of real numbers satisfying $a < x < b$'.

the interval $-2 < x < 2$, in which both endpoints are *excluded*, is denoted by $(-2, 2)$ and is an example of an *open* interval;

In some texts the notation $]-2, 2[$ is used instead of $(-2, 2)$.

the interval $-2 \leq x \leq 2$, in which both endpoints are *included*, is denoted by $[-2, 2]$ and is an example of a *closed* interval.

We use the symbol ∞ when an interval extends indefinitely far to the right on the real line; for example,

The symbol ∞ (infinity) does not denote a real number.

the set of all real numbers greater than -3 is denoted by $(-3, \infty)$.

Similarly, we use the symbol $-\infty$ when an interval extends indefinitely far to the left on the real line; for example,

the set of all real numbers less than or equal to 5 is denoted by $(-\infty, 5]$.

More generally, we adopt the following notation.

Notation Intervals are denoted as follows.

open intervals

(a, b)	(a, ∞)	$(-\infty, b)$	$(-\infty, \infty)$
$a < x < b$	$x > a$	$x < b$	$\mathbb{R}$

closed intervals

$[a, b]$	$[a, \infty)$	$(-\infty, b]$	$(-\infty, \infty)$
$a \leq x \leq b$	$x \geq a$	$x \leq b$	$\mathbb{R}$

half-open (or half-closed) intervals

$[a, b)$	$(a, b]$
$a \leq x < b$	$a < x \leq b$

In the diagrams, an open circle ∘ indicates that an endpoint is excluded, and a solid circle • indicates that an endpoint is included.

We also use (a, b) to denote the Cartesian coordinates of a point in the plane, but in most cases it should be obvious whether a point or an interval is intended.

An interval such as $[a, \infty)$ is regarded as closed, rather than half-open (or half-closed), because it contains *all* the real numbers greater than or equal to a. The interval $\mathbb{R} = (-\infty, \infty)$ is considered to be both open and closed.

Exercise 1.2 For each of the functions defined in Exercise 1.1, write down the interval(s) on which the function is defined.

1.2 Graphs of basic functions

When sketching a graph by hand, we do not aim to achieve the detail possible with a computer plot; rather, we aim to provide a visual summary of the main properties of the function. Before moving on to more complicated functions, we remind you of various basic functions whose graphs you need to be able to recognise and sketch quickly, and we indicate the important features of their graphs. We also review the way in which you can sketch the graphs of other functions that are related to these basic functions. Finally, we remind you of the relationship between certain properties of a function and special features of its graph, and we raise some questions that will be answered in the analysis blocks.

This audio section is rather long. We suggest that you take a break after you have checked your solution to the exercise in Frame 13.

Listen to the audio as you work through the frames.

Audio

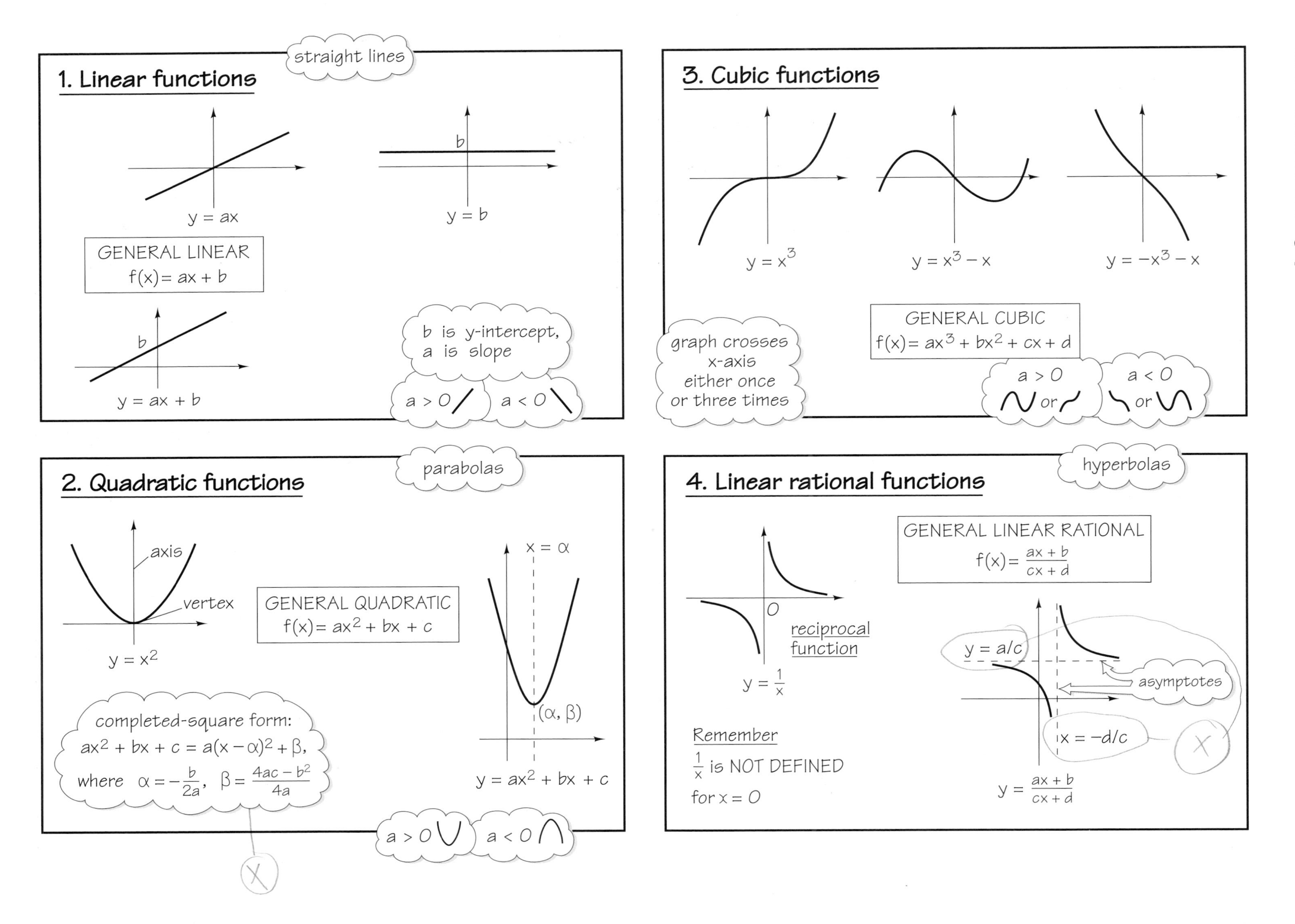
1. Linear functions
straight lines
y = ax
y = b
b
GENERAL LINEAR
f(x) = ax + b
b
y = ax + b
b is y-intercept,
a is slope
a > 0
a < 0
3. Cubic functions
y = x³
y = x³ − x
y = −x³ − x
GENERAL CUBIC
f(x) = ax³ + bx² + cx + d
graph crosses
x-axis
either once
or three times
a > 0
or
a < 0
or
2. Quadratic functions
parabolas
axis
vertex
y = x²
GENERAL QUADRATIC
f(x) = ax² + bx + c
x = α
(α, β)
y = ax² + bx + c
completed-square form:
ax² + bx + c = a(x − α)² + β,
where α = −b/2a, β = (4ac − b²)/4a
a > 0
a < 0
4. Linear rational functions
hyperbolas
GENERAL LINEAR RATIONAL
f(x) = (ax + b)/(cx + d)
O
reciprocal
function
y = 1/x
y = a/c
asymptotes
x = −d/c
y = (ax + b)/(cx + d)
Remember
1/x is NOT DEFINED
for x = 0

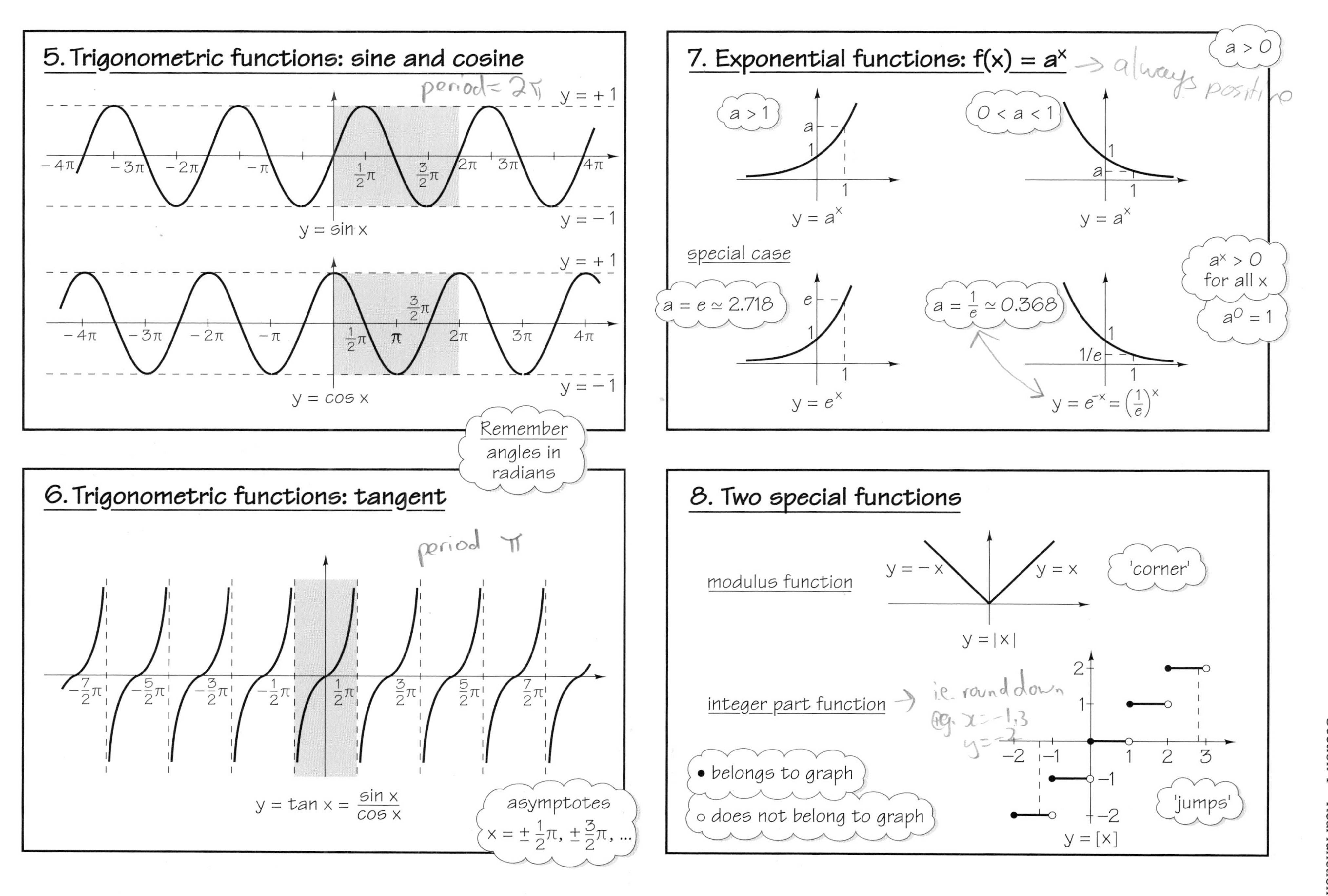

5. Trigonometric functions: sine and cosine
period = 2π
y = +1
y = −1
−4π −3π −2π −π ½π 3/2π 2π 3π 4π
y = sin x
y = +1
y = −1
−4π −3π −2π −π ½π π 3/2π 2π 3π 4π
y = cos x
Remember angles in radians
6. Trigonometric functions: tangent
period π
−7/2π −5/2π −3/2π −½π ½π 3/2π 5/2π 7/2π
y = tan x = sin x / cos x
asymptotes x = ±½π, ±3/2π, ...
7. Exponential functions: f(x) = a^x → always positive
a > 0
a > 1
y = a^x
0 < a < 1
y = a^x
special case
a = e ≃ 2.718
y = e^x
a = 1/e ≃ 0.368
1/e
y = e^−x = (1/e)^x
a^x > 0 for all x
a^0 = 1
8. Two special functions
modulus function
y = −x
y = x
y = |x|
'corner'
integer part function → ie. round down
eg. x = −1.3 y = −2
y = [x]
'jumps'
• belongs to graph
○ does not belong to graph

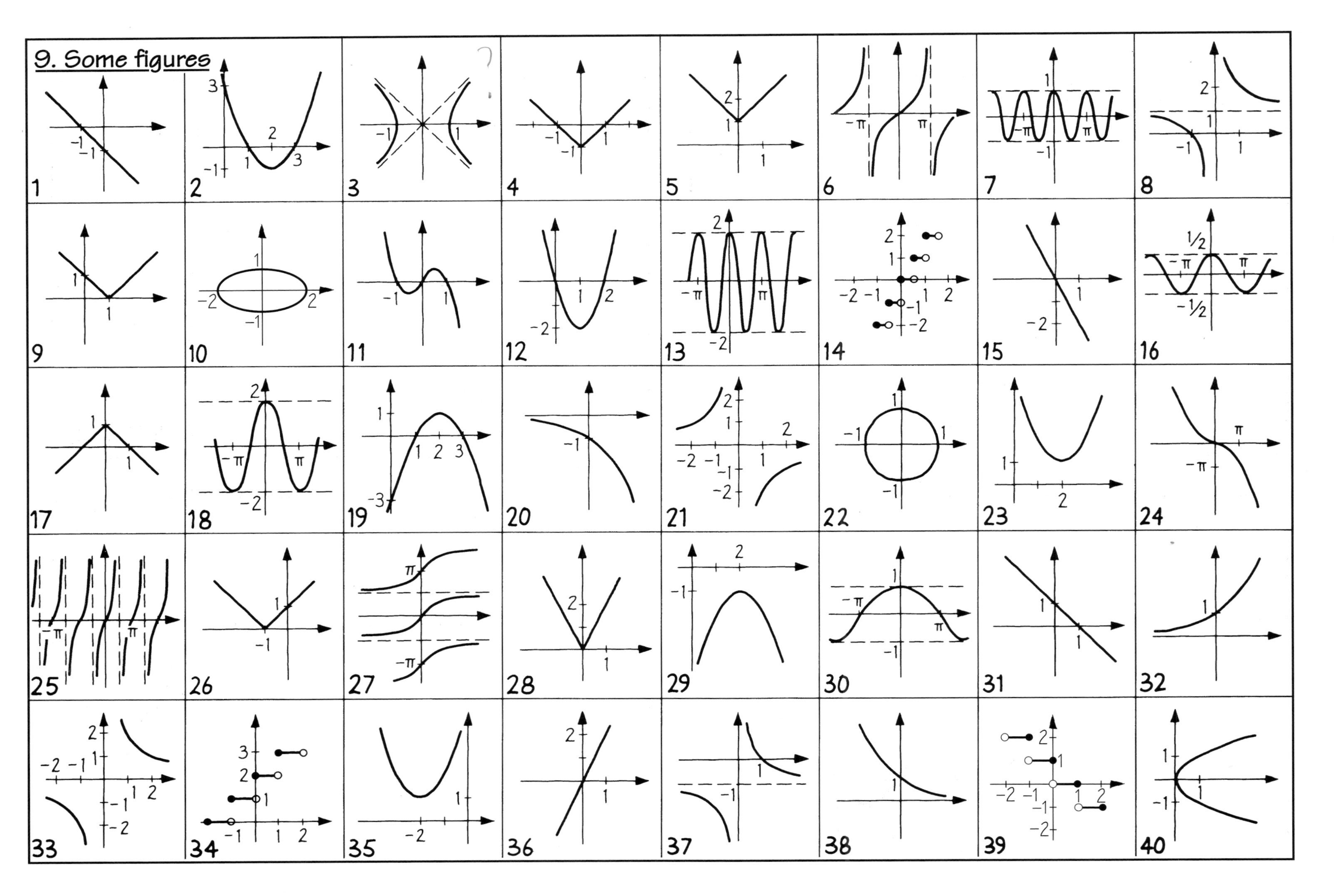
9. Some figures

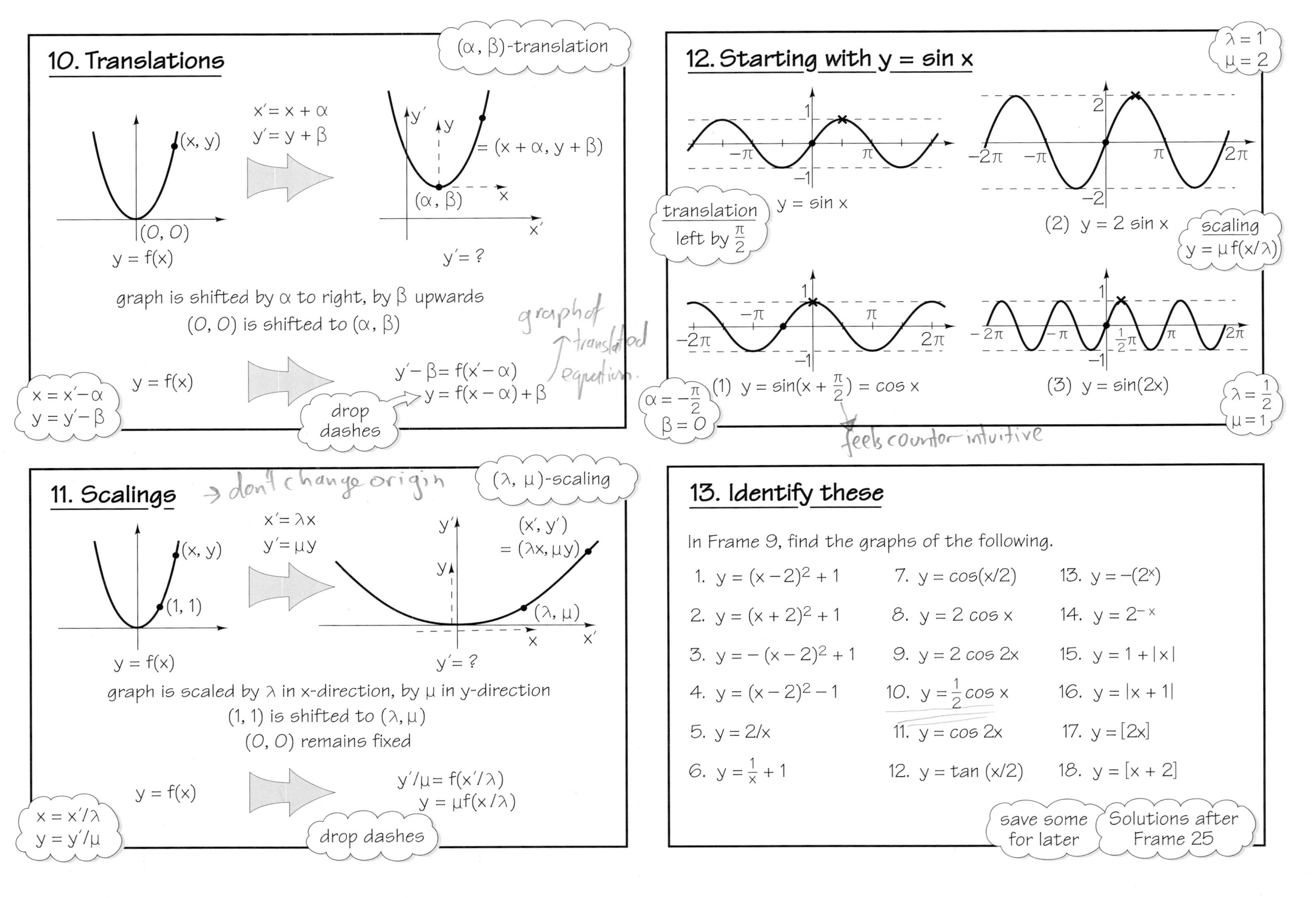
10. Translations
(α, β)-translation
$x' = x + \alpha$
$y' = y + \beta$
(x, y)
$(0, 0)$
$y = f(x)$
$= (x + \alpha, y + \beta)$
(α, β)
$y' = ?$
graph is shifted by α to right, by β upwards
$(0, 0)$ is shifted to (α, β)
$y = f(x)$
$y' - \beta = f(x' - \alpha)$
$y = f(x - \alpha) + \beta$
drop dashes
$x = x' - \alpha$
$y = y' - \beta$
graph of translated equation
11. Scalings
don't change origin
(λ, μ)-scaling
$x' = \lambda x$
$y' = \mu y$
(x, y)
$(1, 1)$
$y = f(x)$
$(x', y') = (\lambda x, \mu y)$
(λ, μ)
$y' = ?$
graph is scaled by λ in x-direction, by μ in y-direction
$(1, 1)$ is shifted to (λ, μ)
$(0, 0)$ remains fixed
$y = f(x)$
$y'/\mu = f(x'/\lambda)$
$y = \mu f(x/\lambda)$
drop dashes
$x = x'/\lambda$
$y = y'/\mu$
12. Starting with $y = \sin x$
$\lambda = 1$
$\mu = 2$
$y = \sin x$
translation left by $\frac{\pi}{2}$
(2) $y = 2 \sin x$
scaling
$y = \mu f(x/\lambda)$
(1) $y = \sin(x + \frac{\pi}{2}) = \cos x$
$\alpha = -\frac{\pi}{2}$
$\beta = 0$
feels counter-intuitive
(3) $y = \sin(2x)$
$\lambda = \frac{1}{2}$
$\mu = 1$
13. Identify these
In Frame 9, find the graphs of the following.
1. $y = (x - 2)^2 + 1$
2. $y = (x + 2)^2 + 1$
3. $y = -(x - 2)^2 + 1$
4. $y = (x - 2)^2 - 1$
5. $y = 2/x$
6. $y = \frac{1}{x} + 1$
7. $y = \cos(x/2)$
8. $y = 2 \cos x$
9. $y = 2 \cos 2x$
10. $y = \frac{1}{2} \cos x$
11. $y = \cos 2x$
12. $y = \tan (x/2)$
13. $y = -(2^x)$
14. $y = 2^{-x}$
15. $y = 1 + |x|$
16. $y = |x + 1|$
17. $y = [2x]$
18. $y = [x + 2]$
save some for later
Solutions after Frame 25

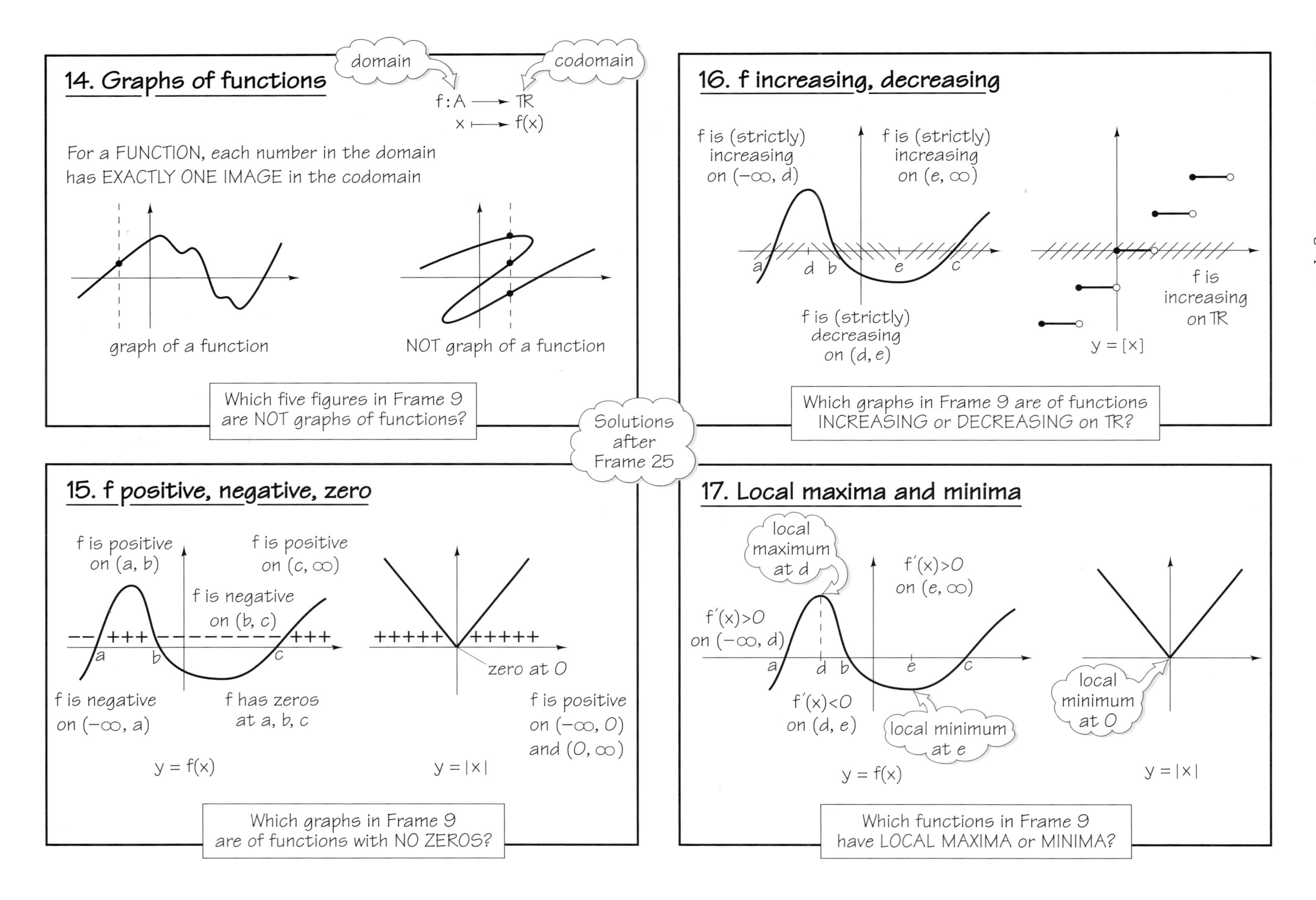
14. Graphs of functions
domain
codomain
f : A ⟶ ℝ
x ⟼ f(x)
For a FUNCTION, each number in the domain has EXACTLY ONE IMAGE in the codomain
graph of a function
NOT graph of a function
Which five figures in Frame 9 are NOT graphs of functions?
16. f increasing, decreasing
f is (strictly) increasing on (−∞, d)
f is (strictly) increasing on (e, ∞)
a d b e c
f is (strictly) decreasing on (d, e)
f is increasing on ℝ
y = [x]
Which graphs in Frame 9 are of functions INCREASING or DECREASING on ℝ?
Solutions after Frame 25
15. f positive, negative, zero
f is positive on (a, b)
f is positive on (c, ∞)
f is negative on (b, c)
a b c
f is negative on (−∞, a)
f has zeros at a, b, c
y = f(x)
zero at O
f is positive on (−∞, O) and (O, ∞)
y = |x|
Which graphs in Frame 9 are of functions with NO ZEROS?
17. Local maxima and minima
local maximum at d
f′(x)>0 on (e, ∞)
f′(x)>0 on (−∞, d)
a d b e c
f′(x)<0 on (d, e)
local minimum at e
y = f(x)
local minimum at O
y = |x|
Which functions in Frame 9 have LOCAL MAXIMA or MINIMA?

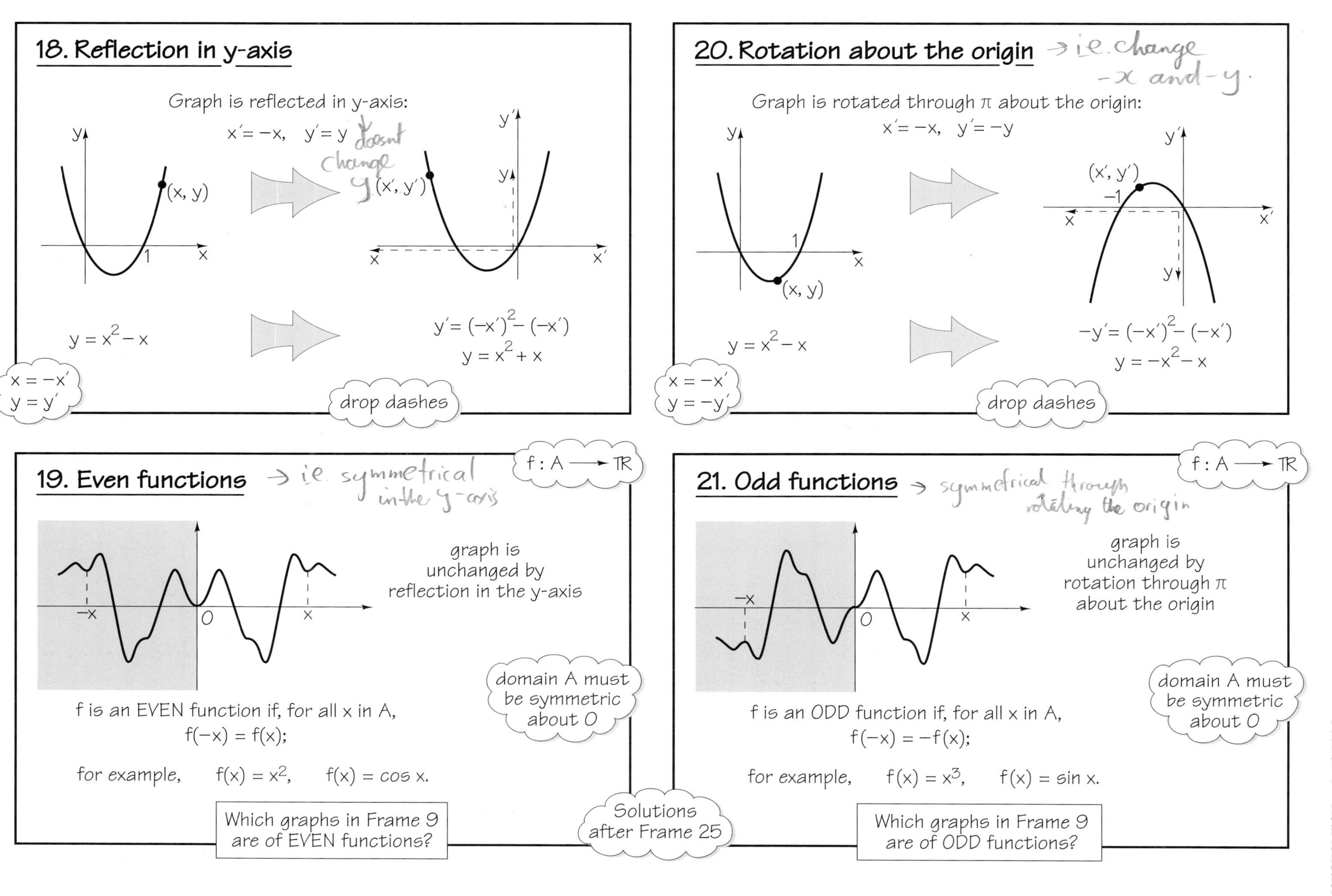
18. Reflection in y-axis
Graph is reflected in y-axis:
x′ = −x, y′ = y
y doesn't change
y
x
1
(x, y)
y′
y
x
x′
(x′, y′)
y = x² − x
y′ = (−x′)² − (−x′)
y = x² + x
x = −x′
y = y′
drop dashes
19. Even functions
i.e. symmetrical in the y-axis
f : A ⟶ ℝ
−x
O
x
graph is
unchanged by
reflection in the y-axis
domain A must
be symmetric
about O
f is an EVEN function if, for all x in A,
f(−x) = f(x);
for example, f(x) = x², f(x) = cos x.
Which graphs in Frame 9
are of EVEN functions?
Solutions
after Frame 25
20. Rotation about the origin
i.e. change −x and −y.
Graph is rotated through π about the origin:
x′ = −x, y′ = −y
y
x
1
(x, y)
y′
x
x′
y
(x′, y′)
−1
y = x² − x
−y′ = (−x′)² − (−x′)
y = −x² − x
x = −x′
y = −y′
drop dashes
21. Odd functions
symmetrical through rotating the origin
f : A ⟶ ℝ
−x
O
x
graph is
unchanged by
rotation through π
about the origin
domain A must
be symmetric
about O
f is an ODD function if, for all x in A,
f(−x) = −f(x);
for example, f(x) = x³, f(x) = sin x.
Which graphs in Frame 9
are of ODD functions?

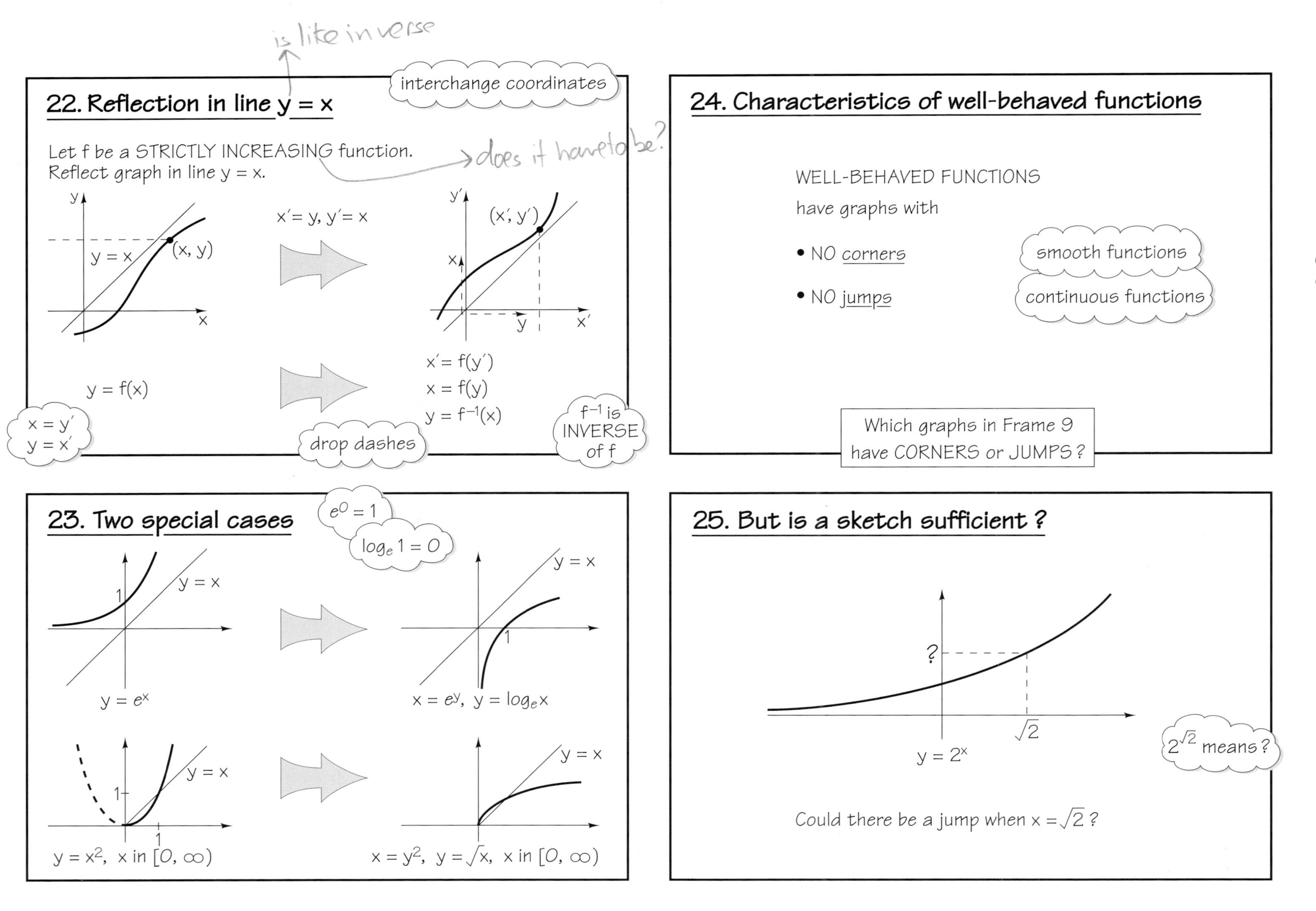
22. Reflection in line y = x
interchange coordinates
is like inverse
Let f be a STRICTLY INCREASING function.
Reflect graph in line y = x.
does it have to be?
y = x
(x, y)
x′ = y, y′ = x
(x′, y′)
y = f(x)
x′ = f(y′)
x = f(y)
y = f⁻¹(x)
x = y′
y = x′
drop dashes
f⁻¹ is INVERSE of f
24. Characteristics of well-behaved functions
WELL-BEHAVED FUNCTIONS
have graphs with
• NO corners
• NO jumps
smooth functions
continuous functions
Which graphs in Frame 9 have CORNERS or JUMPS?
23. Two special cases
e⁰ = 1
log_e 1 = 0
y = x
y = e^x
x = e^y, y = log_e x
y = x², x in [0, ∞)
x = y², y = √x, x in [0, ∞)
25. But is a sketch sufficient?
?
√2
y = 2^x
2^√2 means?
Could there be a jump when x = √2?

Solutions to questions in the audio section

Frame 13

	Function	Type	Transformation		Number
1.	$y = (x-2)^2 + 1$	quadratic	translation	$(\alpha = 2,\ \beta = 1)$	23
2.	$y = (x+2)^2 + 1$	quadratic	translation	$(\alpha = -2,\ \beta = 1)$	35
3.	$y = -(x-2)^2 + 1$	quadratic	scaling	$(\lambda = 1,\ \mu = -1)$	
			translation	$(\alpha = 2,\ \beta = 1)$	19
4.	$y = (x-2)^2 - 1$	quadratic	translation	$(\alpha = 2,\ \beta = -1)$	2
5.	$y = 2/x$	reciprocal	scaling	$(\lambda = 1,\ \mu = 2)$	33
6.	$y = 1/x + 1$	reciprocal	translation	$(\alpha = 0,\ \beta = 1)$	8
7.	$y = \cos(x/2)$	cosine	scaling	$(\lambda = 2,\ \mu = 1)$	30
8.	$y = 2\cos x$	cosine	scaling	$(\lambda = 1,\ \mu = 2)$	18
9.	$y = 2\cos 2x$	cosine	scaling	$(\lambda = \frac{1}{2},\ \mu = 2)$	13
10.	$y = \frac{1}{2}\cos x$	cosine	scaling	$(\lambda = 1,\ \mu = \frac{1}{2})$	16
11.	$y = \cos 2x$	cosine	scaling	$(\lambda = \frac{1}{2},\ \mu = 1)$	7
12.	$y = \tan(x/2)$	tangent	scaling	$(\lambda = 2,\ \mu = 1)$	6
13.	$y = -(2^x)$	exponential	scaling	$(\lambda = 1,\ \mu = -1)$	20
14.	$y = 2^{-x}$	exponential	scaling	$(\lambda = -1,\ \mu = 1)$	38
15.	$y = 1 + \lvert x\rvert$	modulus	translation	$(\alpha = 0,\ \beta = 1)$	5
16.	$y = \lvert x+1\rvert$	modulus	translation	$(\alpha = -1,\ \beta = 0)$	26
17.	$y = [2x]$	integer part	scaling	$(\lambda = \frac{1}{2},\ \mu = 1)$	14
18.	$y = [x+2]$	integer part	translation	$(\alpha = -2,\ \beta = 0)$	34

Frame 14

Figures 3, 10, 22, 27 and 40 are *not* graphs of functions.

Frame 15

Graphs 5, 20, 21, 23, 29, 32, 33, 35, 38 are graphs of functions which have no zeros.

Frame 16

Increasing functions on $\mathbb{R}$: graphs 14, 32, 34, 36; only graphs 32 and 36 are strictly increasing on $\mathbb{R}$.

Decreasing functions on $\mathbb{R}$: graphs 1, 15, 20, 24, 31, 38, 39; all but graph 39 are strictly decreasing on $\mathbb{R}$.

Frame 17

Functions with local maxima and local minima: graphs 7, 11, 13, 16, 18, 30.
Functions with only a local maximum: graphs 17, 19, 29.
Functions with only a local minimum: graphs 2, 4, 5, 9, 12, 23, 26, 28, 35.

Frame 19

Even functions: graphs 4, 5, 7, 13, 16, 17, 18, 28, 30.

Frame 21

Odd functions: graphs 6, 11, 15, 21, 24, 25, 33, 36.

Frame 24

Functions with 'corners': graphs 4, 5, 9, 17, 26, 28.
Functions with 'jumps': graphs 14, 34, 39.

2 Graph sketching

After working through this section, you should be able to:

(a) determine the x-intercepts and y-intercept of a given function f;
(b) determine the intervals on which a given function f is *positive* or *negative*;
(c) determine the intervals on which a given function f is *increasing* or *decreasing*, and any points at which f has a *local maximum* or *local minimum*;
(d) describe the *asymptotic behaviour* (if any) of a given function f;
(e) sketch the graph of a given function.

know

In this section we consider the problem of sketching the graphs of functions that are rather more complicated than the basic functions. We develop the ideas introduced in the previous section, and give a general strategy that will enable you to sketch many graphs.

The aim of sketching the graph of a function is to provide a visual summary of the main properties of the function. Consider, for example, the function

$$f(x) = \frac{1}{1-x^2}.$$

By our convention, the domain of this function is the set of all real numbers excluding 1 and -1; it consists of the three intervals $(-\infty, -1)$, $(-1, 1)$ and $(1, \infty)$.

A sketch of the graph of this function is shown below.

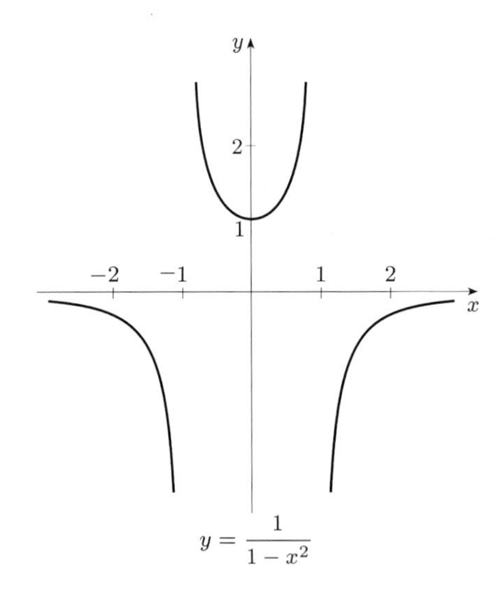

Several key properties of the function f can be seen from this graph.

1. The domain of f consists of the three intervals

   $$(-\infty, -1), \quad (-1, 1), \quad (1, \infty).$$

2. The graph is symmetric about the y-axis, so f is even.
3. The graph of f crosses the y-axis when $y = f(0) = 1$;
   The graph of f does not cross the x-axis.

4. f takes positive values on the interval $(-1, 1)$;
   f takes negative values on the intervals $(-\infty, -1)$ and $(1, \infty)$.
5. f is increasing on the intervals $(0, 1)$ and $(1, \infty)$;
   f is decreasing on the intervals $(-\infty, -1)$ and $(-1, 0)$;
   f has a local minimum at 0.
6. As x approaches 1 from the left or -1 from the right, $f(x)$ becomes very large and positive;

   as x approaches 1 from the right or -1 from the left, $f(x)$ becomes very large and negative;

   as x becomes large and positive or large and negative, $f(x)$ gets closer and closer to 0.

When sketching a graph, we do not aim to achieve the detailed accuracy of a computer plot, but instead to represent important features such as those listed above. But how do we identify these features?

2.1 Determining features of a graph

We discuss how to determine the possible features of a graph in turn.

Domain

When the domain of a function is not given, we use our convention and take the domain to be the set of all real numbers for which the given rule is applicable. So the domain is the set of all real numbers, excluding any numbers which give an expression which is not defined—for example, a zero in the denominator of a rational function, or the square root of a negative number.

'Symmetry' features

In the audio section, we saw that a graph may possess certain types of symmetry:

- For a **periodic function**, such as a trigonometric function, the graph is unchanged by a translation along the x-axis through the period, p say:

  $$f(x + p) = f(x).$$

- For an **even function**, the graph is unchanged by reflection in the y-axis:

  $$f(-x) = f(x).$$

- For an **odd function**, the graph is unchanged by rotation through an angle π about the origin:

  $$f(-x) = -f(x).$$

Intercepts

An **intercept** is a value of x or y at which the graph $y = f(x)$ of a function f meets the x- or y-axis, respectively. The x-intercepts are the solutions (if any) of the equation $f(x) = 0$ and are also known as the **zeros** of f. The y-intercept is the value $f(0)$, if this exists.

It is usually straightforward to find the y-intercept, but harder to find the x-intercepts, since this involves solving the equation $f(x) = 0$. This equation is not always possible to solve algebraically, but it is usually possible to obtain estimates for the solutions by finding intervals of the domain in which the values of the function f change sign.

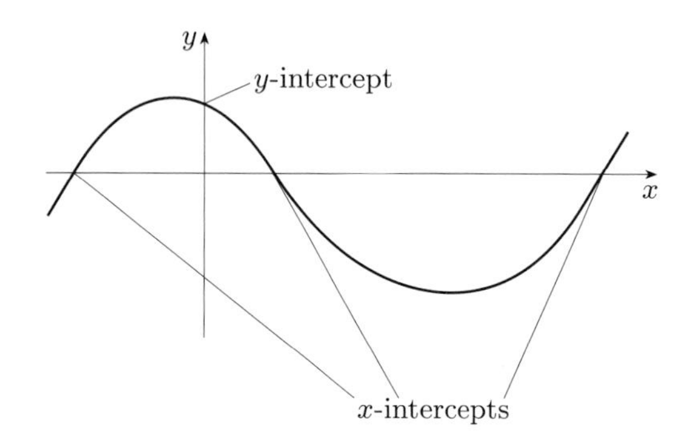

Intervals on which a function has constant sign

We now consider how to determine the intervals on which the values of a function have constant sign. We make the following definitions.

> **Definitions** Let f be a real function with domain A. Then
>
> f is **positive** on an interval I in A if $f(x) > 0$ for all x in I;
>
> f is **negative** on an interval I in A if $f(x) < 0$ for all x in I;
>
> f has a **zero** at the point a in A if $f(a) = 0$.

Sometimes we can find the intervals on which a polynomial or rational function has constant sign by constructing a **sign table** for $f(x)$.

For example, consider the function

$$f(x) = \frac{1}{1 - x^2}.$$

We can factorise $f(x)$:

$$f(x) = \frac{1}{(1 - x)(1 + x)},$$

and construct the following sign table. In the left-hand column of the table are the factors that appear in $f(x)$. In the top row are the key values of x at which the factors change sign, and the intervals on either side of these key values. The signs of the various factors are shown in the table by +, − or 0, from which the sign of $f(x)$ may be deduced.

x	$(-\infty, -1)$	-1	$(-1, 1)$	1	$(1, \infty)$
$1 - x$	+	+	+	0	−
$1 + x$	−	0	+	+	+
$f(x)$	−	*	+	*	−

We use the symbol $*$ to indicate a point which is not in the domain.

We deduce that

f has no zeros;

f is positive on the interval $(-1, 1)$;

f is negative on the intervals $(-\infty, -1)$ and $(1, \infty)$.

For quadratic functions, if we cannot factorise the function we can sometimes find out whether it always has the same sign by 'completing the square'. If the quadratic function is $ax^2 + bx + c$, we can rewrite it as follows.

Frame 2 of the audio section sets this out as

$$a(x - \alpha)^2 + \beta, \text{ where}$$

$$\alpha = \frac{-b}{2a}, \beta = \frac{4ac - b^2}{4a}.$$

You may, of course, use either formulation as you prefer.

$$ax^2 + bx + c = a\left(x^2 + \frac{b}{a}x\right) + c = a\left(x + \frac{b}{2a}\right)^2 - a\left(\frac{b}{2a}\right)^2 + c$$

So, for example,

$$\begin{aligned} 2x^2 + 12x + 19 &= 2(x^2 + 6x) + 19 \\ &= 2(x+3)^2 - 2 \times 3^2 + 19 \\ &= 2(x+3)^2 + 1. \end{aligned}$$

From this, we can see that, whatever the value of x,

$$2x^2 + 12x + 19 = 2(x+3)^2 + 1$$

is always positive.

Exercise 2.1 Complete the square on the following quadratic functions.

(a) $x^2 - 6x + 11$ (b) $3x^2 + 12x - 1$

Intervals on which a function is increasing or decreasing

We referred to functions which are increasing or decreasing on a particular interval in Section 1, but did not give a definition. We now do this.

Definitions

A function f is **increasing** on an interval I, if for all $x_1, x_2 \in I$,

if $x_1 < x_2$, then $f(x_1) \leq f(x_2)$.

A function f is **strictly increasing** on an interval I, if for all $x_1, x_2 \in I$,

if $x_1 < x_2$, then $f(x_1) < f(x_2)$.

A function f is **decreasing** on an interval I, if for all $x_1, x_2 \in I$,

if $x_1 < x_2$, then $f(x_1) \geq f(x_2)$.

A function f is **strictly decreasing** on an interval I, if for all $x_1, x_2 \in I$,

if $x_1 < x_2$, then $f(x_1) > f(x_2)$.

We can sometimes determine the intervals on which a function is increasing or decreasing by inspection of the rule of the function. For example, the function $f(x) = x^3$ is increasing on $\mathbb{R}$ because x^3 increases as x increases.

What it means to be *differentiable* will be defined in the analysis blocks. For the moment you can assume that a function is differentiable if it can be differentiated by the usual methods.

For a differentiable function, however, we can use the derivative of the function to identify these intervals.

Increasing/decreasing criterion

1. If $f'(x) > 0$ for all x in an interval I, then f is (strictly) increasing on I.
2. If $f'(x) < 0$ for all x in an interval I, then f is (strictly) decreasing on I.

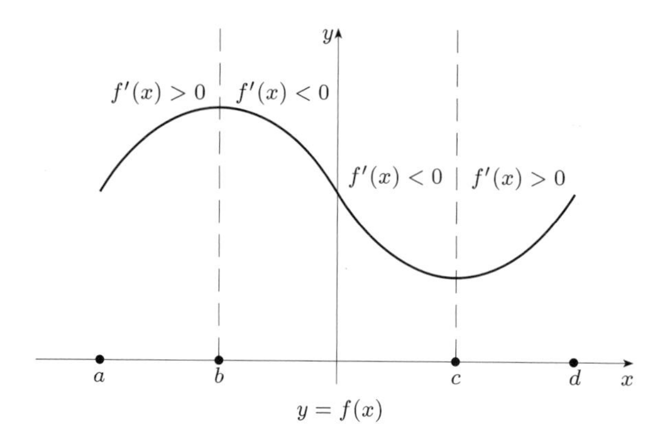

f is (strictly) increasing on the intervals (a, b) and (c, d).

f is (strictly) decreasing on the interval (b, c).

$f'(b) = f'(c) = 0$.

We can determine the intervals on which f is increasing or decreasing by drawing up a sign table for $f'(x)$. The table should also include points a at which $f'(a) = 0$. Such a point is called a **stationary point** of f; it is a value a such that the tangent to the graph is horizontal at the point $(a, f(a))$.

A stationary point need not be a local maximum or a local minimum. For example, $f(x) = x^3$ has a stationary point at 0, with $f(0) = 0$, but has neither a local maximum nor a local minimum at 0. In fact, it has what we call a *horizontal point of inflection*.

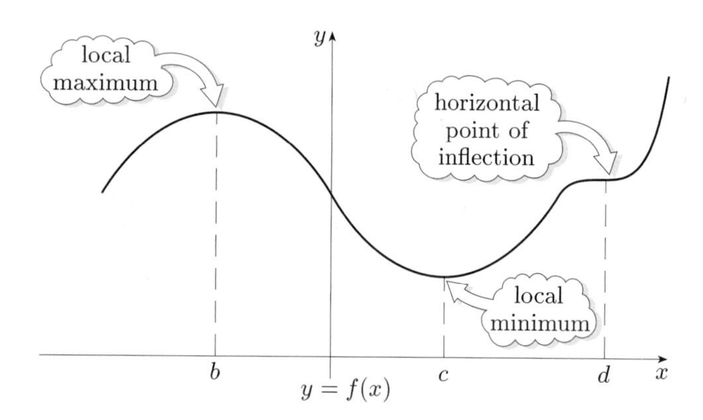

f has a local maximum at b.

f has a local minimum at c.

f has a horizontal point of inflection at d.

We can check whether a stationary point is a local maximum, a local minimum or a horizontal point of inflection by using the following test.

First Derivative Test Suppose that a is a stationary point of a differentiable function f; that is, $f'(a) = 0$.

- If $f'(x)$ changes from positive to negative as x increases through a, then f has a **local maximum** at a.
- If $f'(x)$ changes from negative to positive as x increases through a, then f has a **local minimum** at a.
- If $f'(x)$ remains positive or remains negative as x increases through a (except at a itself, where $f'(a) = 0$), then f has a **horizontal point of inflection** at a.

$f'(x)$ may do none of these things.

Let us return to the function $f(x) = \dfrac{1}{1 - x^2}$. To find the intervals on which the function is increasing and decreasing we use the quotient rule to give

$$f'(x) = -\frac{-2x}{(1 - x^2)^2} = \frac{2x}{(1 - x^2)^2}.$$

You will find a table of standard derivatives in the Handbook, and also a list of the rules for differentiating functions. We assume that you have met differentiation in your previous mathematical studies.

The sign table for $f'(x)$ is as follows.

x	$(-\infty,-1)$	-1	$(-1,0)$	0	$(0,1)$	1	$(1,\infty)$
$2x$	$-$	$-$	$-$	0	$+$	$+$	$+$
$(1-x^2)^2$	$+$	0	$+$	$+$	$+$	0	$+$
$f'(x)$	$-$	$*$	$-$	0	$+$	$*$	$+$

In this case there is no need to factorise $(1-x^2)^2$, since
$(1-x^2)^2 \geq 0$.

We find that

f has a stationary point at 0;
f is increasing on the intervals $(0,1)$ and $(1,\infty)$;
f is decreasing on the intervals $(-\infty,-1)$ and $(-1,0)$.

We deduce that f has a local minimum at 0, by the First Derivative Test.

Asymptotic behaviour of functions

For a function f, the term **asymptotic behaviour** refers to the behaviour of points on the graph of $y = f(x)$ for which the variable x or the variable y take arbitrarily large values.

For example, we consider how to determine the features of the graph of the function $f(x) = \dfrac{1}{1-x^2}$ as x or y approaches ∞.

The computer plot shown on the left below uses a 'join-the-dots' approach to generate the graph of this function. The computer plot is inaccurate near the 'missing' points $x = 1$ and $x = -1$, since it shows vertical lines at $x = 1$ and $x = -1$ as parts of the graph, whereas we know that the function is not defined at these points. It is common for computer plots of graphs to give misleading results near such 'difficult' points. By contrast, the sketch of this graph on the right indicates the behaviour of the function f near the points 1 and -1 by the use of broken vertical lines.

A computer plot always assumes that the curve has no breaks, and tries to join the curve up accordingly.

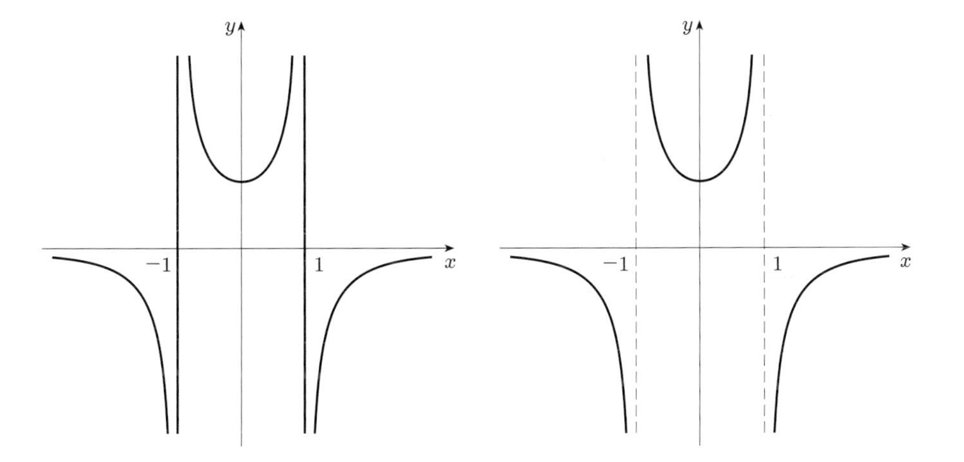

The plot on the left was generated by Mathcad. We have added axes for clarity.

A broken line is used when the graph of a function has an **asymptote**—that is, a straight line which is approached more and more closely by the graph when the domain variable x or the codomain variable y (or both) takes very large values.

An asymptote with an equation of the form $x = a$ is a **vertical asymptote**. For example, in the above graph, the lines $x = -1$ and $x = 1$ are vertical asymptotes.

An asymptote with an equation of the form $y = b$ is a **horizontal asymptote**. For example, in the above graph, the line $y = 0$ is a horizontal asymptote.

When one of the axes is an asymptote, as in this case, it is *not* represented by a broken line.

The behaviour of a function f near a vertical asymptote $x = a$ may take various forms. For the above example, we describe the behaviour near the vertical asymptote $x = -1$ as follows.

> $f(x)$ takes arbitrarily large positive values
> as x tends to -1 from the right;

we write this in symbols as

$$f(x) \to \infty \quad \text{as } x \to -1^+,$$

and read it as

> $f(x)$ tends to infinity as x tends to -1 from the right.

Similarly,

> $f(x)$ takes arbitrarily large negative values
> as x tends to -1 from the left;

we write this in symbols as

$$f(x) \to -\infty \quad \text{as } x \to -1^-,$$

and read it as

> $f(x)$ tends to minus infinity as x tends to -1 from the left.

General versions of these statements are illustrated below, together with similar statements for vertical and for horizontal asymptotes.

Intuitive statements of this nature will be formally defined in Analysis Block A.

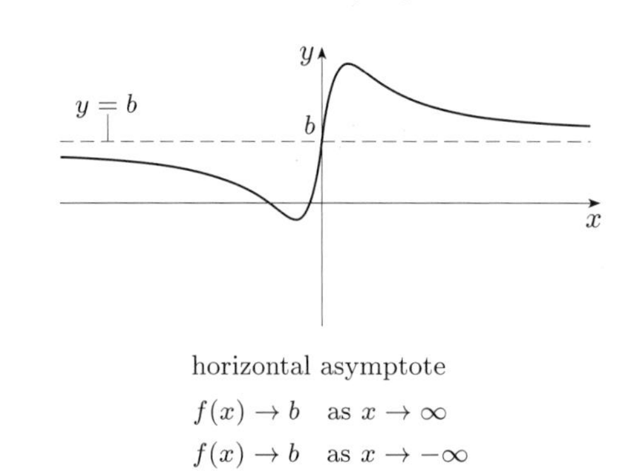

vertical asymptote

$f(x) \to \infty$ as $x \to a^+$

$f(x) \to -\infty$ as $x \to a^-$

horizontal asymptote

$f(x) \to b$ as $x \to \infty$

$f(x) \to b$ as $x \to -\infty$

In the second example, the graph crosses the asymptote.

These diagrams illustrate **asymptotic behaviour**.

Exercise 2.2 Write down four more statements describing the types of asymptotic behaviour displayed by the function $f(x) = \dfrac{1}{1 - x^2}$.

There are other types of behaviour that a function may exhibit as the domain variable x takes large positive or negative values.

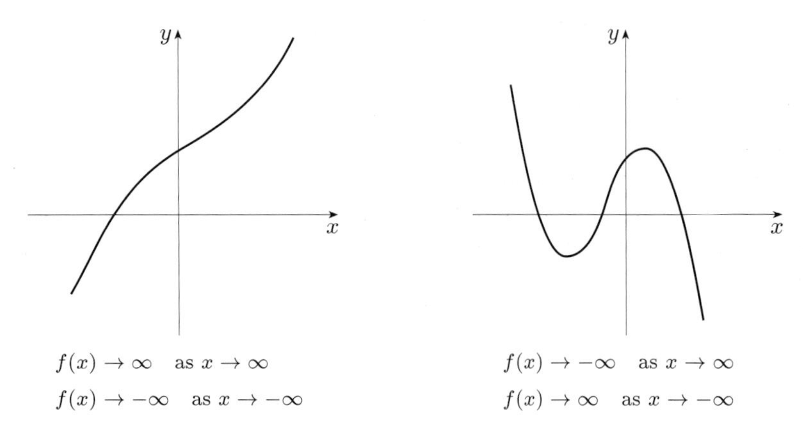

$f(x) \to \infty$ as $x \to \infty$

$f(x) \to -\infty$ as $x \to -\infty$

$f(x) \to -\infty$ as $x \to \infty$

$f(x) \to \infty$ as $x \to -\infty$

Exercise 2.3 Describe the asymptotic behaviour of the following functions.

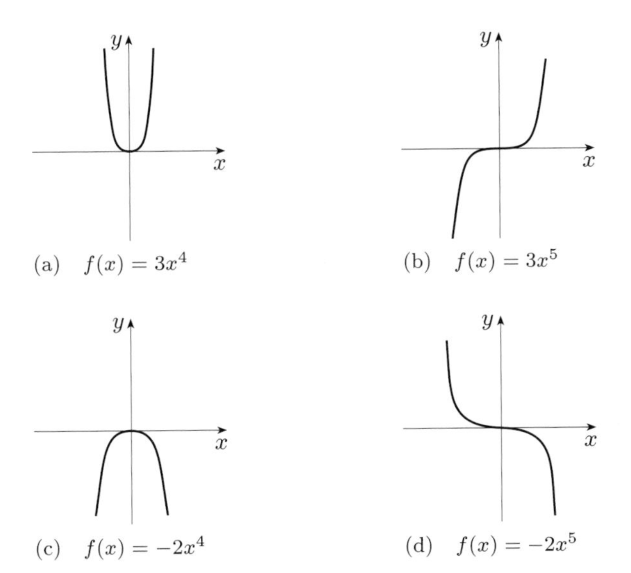

(a) $f(x) = 3x^4$ (b) $f(x) = 3x^5$

(c) $f(x) = -2x^4$ (d) $f(x) = -2x^5$

In general, the behaviour of a **polynomial function of degree** n,

$$f(x) = a_n x^n + a_{n-1}x^{n-1} + \cdots + a_1 x + a_0, \quad \text{where } a_n \neq 0,$$

for large values of x, is similar to that of the term $a_n x^n$. We call x^n the **dominant term**. This behaviour is summarised in the following tables.

It is x^n rather than $a_n x^n$ that we are calling 'the dominant term'. Thus, for example, the expressions $3x^3 - 2x^2 + 1$ and $-4x^3 + 5x - 3$ have the *same* dominant term, namely x^3.

$a_n > 0$	$x \to \infty$	$x \to -\infty$
n even	$f(x) \to \infty$	$f(x) \to \infty$
n odd	$f(x) \to \infty$	$f(x) \to -\infty$

$a_n < 0$	$x \to \infty$	$x \to -\infty$
n even	$f(x) \to -\infty$	$f(x) \to -\infty$
n odd	$f(x) \to -\infty$	$f(x) \to \infty$

A **rational function** is a function defined by a rule of the form

$$x \longmapsto \frac{p(x)}{q(x)},$$

where both p and q are polynomial functions. Locating vertical and horizontal asymptotes is an important step in sketching the graph of any rational function. Vertical asymptotes occur at the values of x for which $q(x) = 0$ and $p(x) \neq 0$, and horizontal asymptotes may occur when $x \to \infty$ or $x \to -\infty$.

The function $x \longmapsto \dfrac{1}{1-x^2}$ is an example of a rational function, with $p(x) = 1$ and $q(x) = 1 - x^2$.

To find the behaviour of a rational function for large values of x, we divide both the numerator and denominator by the dominant term of the *denominator*. If the dominant term of the numerator is a *higher power* than that of the denominator, then there will be no horizontal asymptote, whereas if it is a *lower power* than that of the denominator, then the line $y = 0$ will be the horizontal asymptote. The situation is more complicated if the numerator and denominator have the *same* dominant term; this is illustrated by later examples.

if dominant term of the denominator > numerator then there will be a horizontal asymptote

2.2 Strategy for graph sketching

We begin this subsection by summarising basic features which a sketch of a graph should convey, in the form of a strategy, and then we illustrate the strategy with several worked examples.

Strategy 2.1 Graph-sketching strategy

To sketch the graph of a given function f, determine the following features of f (where possible), and show these features in your sketch.

1. The domain of f.
2. Whether f is even, odd or periodic (or none of these).
3. The x-intercepts and y-intercept of f.
4. The intervals on which f is positive or negative.
5. The intervals on which f is increasing or decreasing, the nature of any stationary points, and the value of f at each of these points.
6. The asymptotic behaviour of f.

All the periodic functions that you will meet in this course will involve a trigonometric function (sine, cosine, tangent, cotangent, secant or cosecant), so there is no need to investigate whether f is periodic unless one of these expressions appears in the rule.

Remarks

1. It is important to begin by determining the domain of f. For example, if the domain is $[3, 9]$, then f is neither even nor odd, and you cannot find the behaviour of f as $x \to \infty$.
2. We have numbered the features for easy reference, but it is not necessary to find them in the order given above. Indeed, for some graphs, not all the above features are relevant.

   For some graphs, we can obtain sufficient information without including all the steps. However, it is useful to obtain information in more than one way, in order to provide a check.
3. Choose the scales on your axes with care: usually, the scales should be the same on both axes, but it may be necessary to have unequal scales in order to display some key features of the graph—for example, when $f(x)$ is much larger than x.

Our first example to illustrate Strategy 2.1 is a polynomial function.

Example 2.1 Sketch the graph of the function

$$f(x) = 4x^3 + 3x^2 - 6x + 4.$$

Solution

1. By our convention, the domain of f is $\mathbb{R}$.
2. The function is neither even nor odd, since, for example,

   $$f(1) = 5, \quad \text{but} \quad f(-1) = 9.$$

   There is no trigonometric function involved, so it is not periodic.
3. To find the x-intercepts of f we need to solve the equation $f(x) = 0$, that is

   $$4x^3 + 3x^2 - 6x + 4 = 0.$$

   There are no obvious factors for the expression on the left, so we cannot easily find the zeros. However,

   $$f(-2) = -4 \quad \text{and} \quad f(0) = 4,$$

In future, we shall not normally mention that f is not periodic *unless* a trigonometric function is involved.

We tried various values of x for which $f(x)$ was easy to calculate, and chose these particular values of x because the values of f are positive at one value of x and negative at the other.

so $f(x)$ changes from negative to positive as x increases from -2 to 0. Thus there is an x-intercept in the interval $(-2, 0)$. The y-intercept is $f(0) = 4$.

4. Because we cannot find the zeros of f, we cannot find the intervals on which f is positive or negative. However, we know from step 3 that the sign of f changes from negative to positive as x increases from -2 to 0.

5. Differentiating gives

$$f'(x) = 12x^2 + 6x - 6 = 6(2x^2 + x - 1) = 6(2x - 1)(x + 1).$$

We construct a sign table for $f'(x)$.

x	$(-\infty, -1)$	-1	$(-1, \frac{1}{2})$	$\frac{1}{2}$	$(\frac{1}{2}, \infty)$
$6(2x-1)$	$-$	$-$	$-$	0	$+$
$x+1$	$-$	0	$+$	$+$	$+$
$f'(x)$	$+$	0	$-$	0	$+$

From the sign table we see that

f is increasing on the intervals $(-\infty, -1)$ and $(\frac{1}{2}, \infty)$;
f is decreasing on the interval $(-1, \frac{1}{2})$;
f has stationary points at -1 and $\frac{1}{2}$.

By the First Derivative Test, we deduce that

there is a local maximum at $x = -1$ with $f(-1) = 9$;
there is a local minimum at $x = \frac{1}{2}$ with $f(\frac{1}{2}) = \frac{9}{4}$.

6. The degree of the polynomial function is odd and the coefficient of x^3 is positive, so the first table for the asymptotic behaviour of polynomial functions on page 25 gives

$$f(x) \to \infty \text{ as } x \to \infty \quad \text{and} \quad f(x) \to -\infty \text{ as } x \to -\infty.$$

This information enables us to sketch the graph.

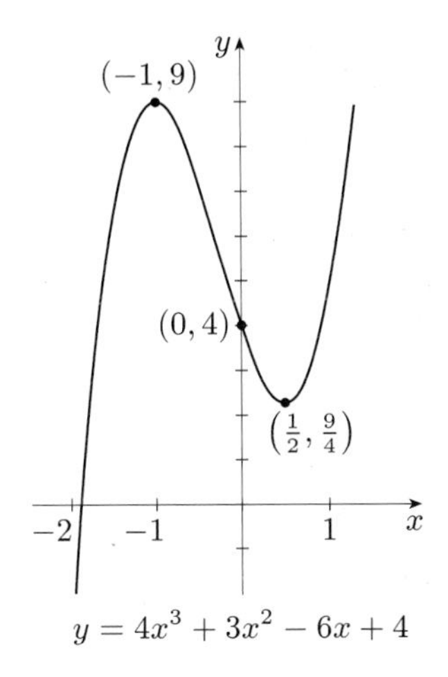

The results of steps 4 and 5 show that the graph of f crosses the x-axis at only one point. ■

Exercise 2.4 Sketch the graph of the polynomial function

$$f(x) = x^4 - 2x^2 + 3.$$

Hint: Putting $t = x^2$, the expression becomes $t^2 - 2t + 3$.

Next, we sketch the graph of a linear rational function.

Example 2.2 Sketch the graph of the function

$$f(x) = \frac{2x-3}{x-1}.$$

Solution

1. By our convention, the domain of f is $\mathbb{R}$, excluding 1; that is, it consists of the intervals $(-\infty, 1)$ and $(1, \infty)$.

2. The function is neither even nor odd, since its domain is not symmetric about 0; for example,

   $$f(-1) = \tfrac{5}{2}, \quad \text{but } f \text{ is not defined at } x = 1.$$

3. $f(x) = 0$ when $2x - 3 = 0$, so the x-intercept is $\frac{3}{2}$. $f(0) = -3/(-1) = 3$, so the y-intercept is 3.

4. We construct a sign table for $f(x)$.

x	$(-\infty, 1)$	1	$(1, \frac{3}{2})$	$\frac{3}{2}$	$(\frac{3}{2}, \infty)$
$2x-3$	$-$	$-$	$-$	0	$+$
$x-1$	$-$	0	$+$	$+$	$+$
$f(x)$	$+$	*	$-$	0	$+$

   So

   f is positive on the intervals $(-\infty, 1)$ and $(\frac{3}{2}, \infty)$;

   f is negative on the interval $(1, \frac{3}{2})$.

5. Using the rule for differentiating a quotient, we obtain

   $$f'(x) = \frac{(x-1)2 - (2x-3)1}{(x-1)^2} = \frac{1}{(x-1)^2}.$$

   The derivative f' is undefined at 1, and $f'(x) > 0$ for $x < 1$ and $x > 1$. Thus

   f is increasing on the intervals $(-\infty, 1)$ and $(1, \infty)$;

   f has no stationary points.

6. The denominator is 0 when $x = 1$, so

   the line $x = 1$ is a vertical asymptote.

   Thus, by the results of step 4 (or step 5),

   $$f(x) \to \infty \text{ as } x \to 1^- \quad \text{and} \quad f(x) \to -\infty \text{ as } x \to 1^+.$$

   From step 4, $f(x)$ is positive as x tends to 1^-, and $f(x)$ is negative as x tends to 1^+.

   To find the behaviour of $f(x)$ for large positive or negative values of x, we divide both the numerator and denominator of $f(x)$ by the dominant term of the denominator, x:

   This division is permitted, since $x \neq 0$.

   $$f(x) = \frac{2x-3}{x-1} = \frac{2-3/x}{1-1/x}.$$

   Now $1/x \to 0$ as $x \to \pm\infty$, so

   We write 'as $x \to \pm\infty$' as shorthand for 'as $x \to \infty$ and as $x \to -\infty$'.

   $$f(x) \to \frac{2-(3 \times 0)}{1-0} = \frac{2-0}{1-0} = 2 \quad \text{as } x \to \pm\infty.$$

   Thus

   the line $y = 2$ is a horizontal asymptote,

   and

   $$f(x) \to 2 \quad \text{as } x \to \pm\infty.$$

This information enables us to sketch the graph.

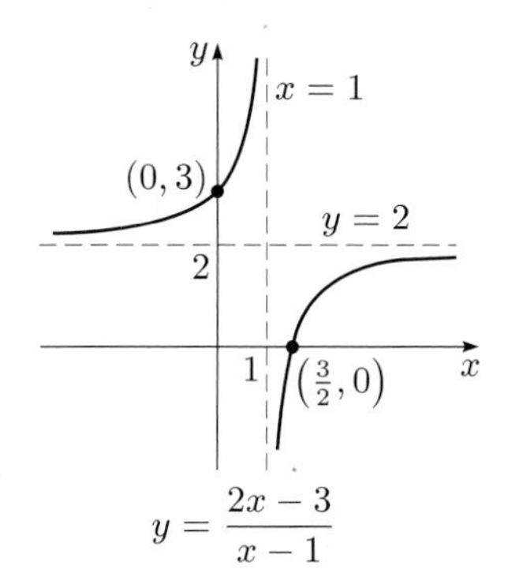

$$y = \frac{2x-3}{x-1}$$

This function can also be written as $f(x) = 2 - \dfrac{1}{x-1}$. ■

Exercise 2.5 Sketch the graph of the linear rational function

$$f(x) = \frac{x-3}{2-x}.$$

Exercise 2.6 Sketch the graph of the linear rational function

$$f(x) = \frac{4x+1}{3x-5}.$$

Next, we sketch the graph of a more complicated rational function.

Example 2.3 Sketch the graph of the function

$$f(x) = \frac{x^2-5x+4}{x^2+5x+4}.$$

Solution

1. We factorise $f(x)$ as follows.

$$f(x) = \frac{x^2-5x+4}{x^2+5x+4} = \frac{(x-1)(x-4)}{(x+1)(x+4)}$$

Thus the domain of f is $\mathbb{R}$, excluding -1 and -4; it consists of the intervals $(-\infty,-4)$, $(-4,-1)$ and $(-1,\infty)$.

2. The function is neither even nor odd, since for example,

$$f(2) = -\tfrac{1}{9}, \quad \text{but } f(-2) = -9.$$

Alternatively, observe that the domain is not symmetric about 0.

3. $f(x) = 0$ when $(x-1)(x-4) = 0$, so the x-intercepts are 1 and 4. $f(0) = 4/4 = 1$, so the y-intercept is 1.

4. We construct a sign table for $f(x)$.

x	$(-\infty,-4)$	-4	$(-4,-1)$	-1	$(-1,1)$	1	$(1,4)$	4	$(4,\infty)$
$x-1$	$-$	$-$	$-$	$-$	$-$	0	$+$	$+$	$+$
$x-4$	$-$	$-$	$-$	$-$	$-$	$-$	$-$	0	$+$
$x+1$	$-$	$-$	$-$	0	$+$	$+$	$+$	$+$	$+$
$x+4$	$-$	0	$+$	$+$	$+$	$+$	$+$	$+$	$+$
$f(x)$	$+$	$*$	$-$	$*$	$+$	0	$-$	0	$+$

So

f is positive on the intervals $(-\infty,-4)$, $(-1,1)$ and $(4,\infty)$;
f is negative on the intervals $(-4,-1)$ and $(1,4)$.

5. Using the quotient rule, we differentiate $f(x)$ as follows.

$$f'(x) = \frac{(2x-5)(x^2+5x+4)-(x^2-5x+4)(2x+5)}{(x^2+5x+4)^2}$$

$$= \frac{(2x^3+10x^2+8x-5x^2-25x-20)-(2x^3-10x^2+8x+5x^2-25x+20)}{(x^2+5x+4)^2}$$

$$= \frac{10(x^2-4)}{(x^2+5x+4)^2}$$

$$= \frac{10(x-2)(x+2)}{(x+1)^2(x+4)^2}$$

We construct a sign table for $f'(x)$.

x	$(-\infty,-4)$	-4	$(-4,-2)$	-2	$(-2,-1)$	-1	$(-1,2)$	2	$(2,\infty)$
$10(x-2)$	$-$	$-$	$-$	$-$	$-$	$-$	$-$	0	$+$
$x+2$	$-$	$-$	$-$	0	$+$	$+$	$+$	$+$	$+$
$(x+1)^2$	$+$	$+$	$+$	$+$	$+$	0	$+$	$+$	$+$
$(x+4)^2$	$+$	0	$+$	$+$	$+$	$+$	$+$	$+$	$+$
$f'(x)$	$+$	$*$	$+$	0	$-$	$*$	$-$	0	$+$

So

f is increasing on the intervals $(-\infty,-4)$, $(-4,-2)$ and $(2,\infty)$;
f is decreasing on the intervals $(-2,-1)$ and $(-1,2)$;
f has stationary points at -2 and 2.

By the First Derivative Test, we deduce that

there is a local maximum at $x=-2$ with $f(-2)=-9$;
there is a local minimum at $x=2$ with $f(2)=-\frac{1}{9}$.

6. The denominator is 0 when $x=-4$ and $x=-1$, so

the line $x=-4$ is a vertical asymptote;
the line $x=-1$ is a vertical asymptote.

Thus, by the results of step 4,

$f(x)\to\infty$ as $x\to-4^-$ and $f(x)\to-\infty$ as $x\to-4^+$;
$f(x)\to-\infty$ as $x\to-1^-$ and $f(x)\to\infty$ as $x\to-1^+$.

To find the behaviour of $f(x)$ for large values of x, we divide both the numerator and denominator of $f(x)$ by the dominant term of the denominator, x^2:

$$f(x) = \frac{1-5/x+4/x^2}{1+5/x+4/x^2}, \quad \text{for } x \neq 0.$$

Now $1/x\to 0$ as $x\to\pm\infty$ and $1/x^2\to 0$ as $x\to\pm\infty$, so

$$f(x) \to \frac{1-(5\times 0)+(4\times 0)}{1+(5\times 0)+(4\times 0)} = \frac{1-0+0}{1+0+0} = 1 \quad \text{as } x\to\pm\infty.$$

Thus

the line $y=1$ is a horizontal asymptote,

and

$f(x)\to 1$ as $x\to\pm\infty$.

This information enables us to sketch the graph.

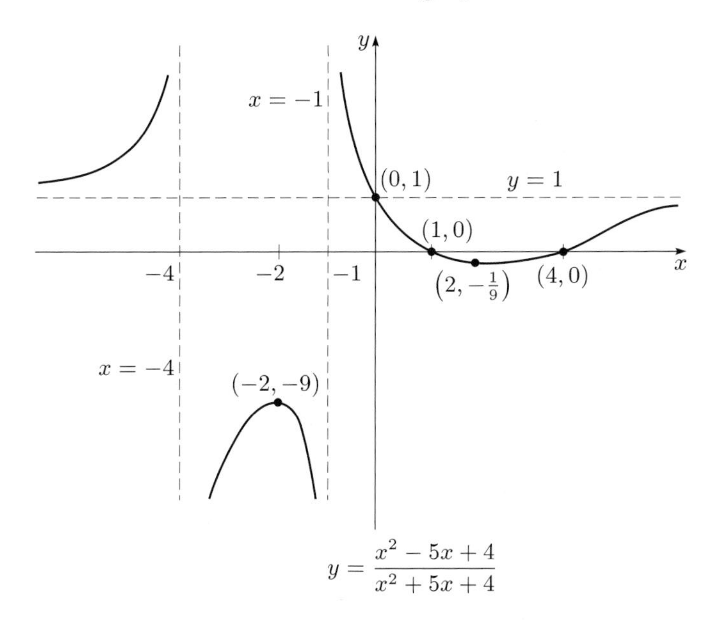

■

Exercise 2.7 Sketch the graph of the rational function

$$f(x) = \frac{1}{x(x+1)^2}.$$

Finally we use Strategy 2.1 to sketch the graph of a function which is not rational.

Example 2.4 Sketch the graph of the function

$$f(x) = \frac{x}{\sqrt{x^2+1}}.$$

Solution

1. The domain of f is $\mathbb{R}$, since $x^2 + 1 > 0$ for all x in $\mathbb{R}$.
2. f is odd, since

$$f(-x) = \frac{-x}{\sqrt{(-x)^2+1}} = \frac{-x}{\sqrt{x^2+1}} = -f(x) \quad \text{for all } x \text{ in } \mathbb{R}.$$

3. The solution of $f(x) = 0$, that is $x/\sqrt{x^2+1} = 0$, is $x = 0$, so the x-intercept and the y-intercept are both 0. That is, the graph crosses the axes only at the origin.
4. Since $f(x)$ has the same sign as x,

   f is positive on the interval $(0, \infty)$;

   f is negative on the interval $(-\infty, 0)$.

5. Using the quotient rule, we obtain

$$f'(x) = \frac{\sqrt{x^2+1} - x\left(\frac{1}{2}(x^2+1)^{-1/2}2x\right)}{x^2+1}$$
$$= \frac{x^2+1-x^2}{(x^2+1)^{3/2}} = \frac{1}{(x^2+1)^{3/2}}.$$

We have multiplied the numerator and denominator by $(x^2+1)^{1/2}$.

So $f'(x) > 0$ for all x in $\mathbb{R}$; that is,

   f is increasing on $\mathbb{R}$.

In addition, $f'(0) = 1$, so the graph has slope 1 at the origin.

Although finding $f'(0)$ is not part of Strategy 2.1, here it is easy to do and helps with the sketch.

6. To find the behaviour of $f(x)$ for large positive values of x, we divide both the numerator and denominator of $f(x)$ by the dominant term of the denominator, x:

$$f(x) = \frac{1}{\sqrt{1+1/x^2}}, \quad \text{for } x > 0.$$

So

$$f(x) \to 1 \quad \text{as } x \to \infty.$$

Thus

the line $y = 1$ is a horizontal asymptote.

Since f is odd,

$$f(x) \to -1 \quad \text{as } x \to -\infty.$$

Thus

the line $y = -1$ is a horizontal asymptote.

Dividing the denominator by x implies that, within the square-root sign, we divide by x^2, and this allows us to determine the limit as $x \to \infty$. Don't worry if you find this tricky to follow: you will not be assessed on such a difficult graph.

This information enables us to sketch the graph.

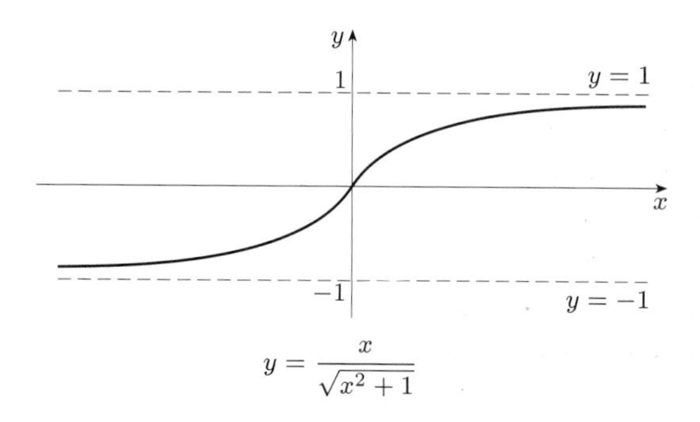

$y = \dfrac{x}{\sqrt{x^2+1}}$ ■

Earlier in this section we introduced the First Derivative Test to determine whether a given stationary point gives a local maximum, local minimum or neither. There is an alternative test for a local maximum or local minimum, using the second derivative of the function f.

You may have met this test if you have studied calculus previously.

> **Second Derivative Test** Suppose that a is a stationary point of a differentiable function f; that is, $f'(a) = 0$.
> 1. If $f''(a) < 0$, then f has a local maximum at a.
> 2. If $f''(a) > 0$, then f has a local minimum at a.

To use this test, f has to be a twice-differentiable function.

This test can be very efficient as a means of classifying stationary points. However, for some functions it is too complicated to find the second derivative. Moreover, if $f''(a) = 0$, then the Second Derivative Test gives no result; the stationary point may be a local maximum, a local minimum, or neither in this case. This is why the Strategy 2.1 uses the First Derivative Test.

Further exercises

Sketch the graph of each of the following functions.

Exercise 2.8 $f(x) = \frac{1}{5}x^5 - x^3$

Exercise 2.9 $f(x) = \dfrac{4x+3}{x-7}$

to do

Exercise 2.10 $f(x) = \dfrac{2x}{x^2 + x - 2}$

Exercise 2.11 $f(x) = \dfrac{1}{\sqrt{1 + x^2}}$

3 New graphs from old

After working through this section, you should be able to:

(a) sketch the graph of a combination of two functions, one of which is a trigonometric function;

(b) sketch the graph of a *hybrid function*, whose rule is defined by different formulas on different parts of its domain.

3.1 Further graph-sketching techniques

We first illustrate some techniques for sketching the graph of a combination of two functions, one of which is a trigonometric function. As far as possible, we follow the steps of Strategy 2.1 but in some examples, part or all of some steps are not necessary. In particular, we try to avoid differentiating anything difficult! We can also exploit the known features of the trigonometric functions, such as the fact that the values of $\sin x$ and $\cos x$ oscillate (with period 2π) between the values 1 and -1. Because of this oscillation it is often convenient to use other simple graphs as construction lines. So, for this subsection, we add another step to Strategy 2.1 as follows.

Strategy 3.1 Extended graph-sketching strategy

To sketch the graph of a given function f, determine the following features of f (where possible), and show these features in your sketch.

1. The domain of f.
2. Whether f is even, odd or periodic (or none of these).
3. The x-intercepts and y-intercept of f.
4. The intervals on which f is positive or negative.
5. The intervals on which f is increasing or decreasing, the nature of any stationary points and the value of f at each of these points.
6. The asymptotic behaviour of f.
7. Any appropriate construction lines, and the points where f meets these lines.

The following example illustrates Strategy 3.1.

Example 3.1 Sketch the graph of the function

$$f(x) = x \sin x.$$

Solution We use Strategy 3.1 as far as possible.

1. The function f has domain $\mathbb{R}$.
2. The function f is even, since $-x\sin(-x) = x\sin x$ for all x in $\mathbb{R}$.

   It is therefore sufficient initially to consider the features of $f(x)$ only for $x \geq 0$ and then to reflect the graph we obtain in the y-axis.
3. $f(x) = 0$ when $x = 0$ and when $\sin x = 0$—that is, when $x = 0, \pi, 2\pi, \ldots$. So the x-intercepts are $0, \pi, 2\pi, \ldots$, and the y-intercept is 0 since $f(0) = 0$.
4. For $x > 0$, the intervals on which f is positive or negative alternate between the above zeros in the same way as for the sine function. That is,

   f is positive on $(0, \pi), (2\pi, 3\pi), \ldots;$
   f is negative on $(\pi, 2\pi), (3\pi, 4\pi), \ldots.$
5. $f'(x) = \sin x + x\cos x$, but $f'(x) = 0$ is not easy to solve, so we shall not use it to find intervals on which f is increasing or decreasing, nor to find local maxima and minima.
6. The function f has no asymptotes as it is defined for all values of x and does not tend to a limit as x tends to $\pm\infty$.
7. Since

   $$-1 \leq \sin x \leq 1, \quad \text{for all real numbers } x,$$

   we have

   $$-x \leq x\sin x \leq x, \quad \text{for } x > 0,$$
   $$-x \geq x\sin x \geq x, \quad \text{for } x < 0.$$

   These inequalities tell us that

   $$-|x| \leq f(x) \leq |x|, \quad \text{for all real numbers } x,$$

   so the graph of f lies between the graphs of the functions $x \longmapsto |x|$ and $x \longmapsto -|x|$. These graphs are the construction lines for this function. The function f has the following features:

   $$f(x) = x = |x| \text{ when } \sin x = 1, \text{ i.e. when } x = \pi/2, 5\pi/2, \ldots;$$
   $$f(x) = -x = -|x| \text{ when } \sin x = -1, \text{ i.e. when } x = 3\pi/2, 7\pi/2, \ldots.$$

   So the graph of $f(x)$

   meets the construction line $|x|$ when $x = \pi/2, 5\pi/2, \ldots;$
   meets the construction line $-|x|$ when $x = 3\pi/2, 7\pi/2, \ldots.$

   To begin the sketch, we draw the construction lines $y = |x|$ and $y = -|x|$. Then we draw dots to indicate the points where the graph of f meets these construction lines and where it crosses the x-axis. We complete the sketch by drawing a smooth curve through these points and then reflecting the graph in the y-axis.

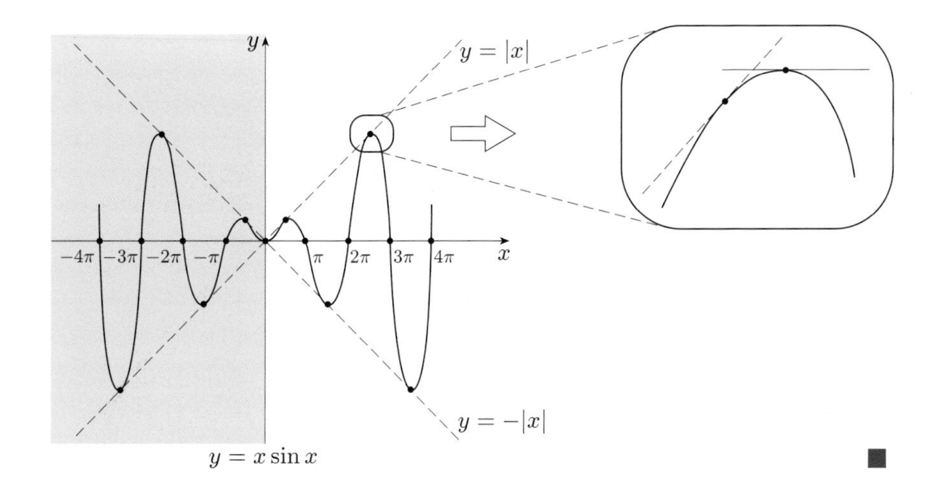

The enlargement illustrates that the dots on $y = |x|$ are not local maxima, and similarly the dots on $y = -|x|$ are not local minima.

■

Exercise 3.1 Sketch the graph of the function $f(x) = x\cos x$.

Exercise 3.2 Sketch the graph of the function $f(x) = x + \sin x$.

Our next example concerns the graph of a composite function.

A **composite function** is a function, such as $f(x) = \sin(1/x)$, which can be obtained by applying first one function (here, $x \longmapsto 1/x$) and then another function (here, $x \longmapsto \sin x$).

Example 3.2 Sketch the graph of the function

$$f(x) = \sin\frac{1}{x}.$$

Solution

1. The domain of f is $\mathbb{R}$ excluding 0; that is, it consists of the intervals $(-\infty, 0)$ and $(0, \infty)$.
2. The function f is odd, since $\sin(1/(-x)) = -\sin(1/x)$ for all $x \neq 0$. So it is sufficient to consider just non-negative values of x and to rotate the graph obtained through π about the origin to obtain the left-hand half.
3. $\sin x = 0$ when $x = 0, \pi, 2\pi, 3\pi, \ldots,$
   so $f(x) = 0$ when $1/x = \pi, 2\pi, 3\pi, \ldots$
   —that is, when $x = 1/\pi, 1/2\pi, 1/3\pi, \ldots.$
   So the x-intercepts are $1/\pi, 1/2\pi, 1/3\pi, \ldots.$

   Since f is not defined when $x = 0$ there is no y-intercept.

The x-intercepts or zeros are ordered from right to left and become closer together as x approaches 0 from the right.

4. If $x > 1/\pi$, then $0 < 1/x < \pi$, so $\sin(1/x) > 0$ and thus f is positive on $(1/\pi, \infty)$. Between 0 and $1/\pi$ the intervals on which f is positive and negative alternate between the zeros found in step 3. Thus f is

   negative on $(1/2\pi, 1/\pi), (1/4\pi, 1/3\pi), \ldots,$

   positive on $(1/3\pi, 1/2\pi), (1/5\pi, 1/4\pi), \ldots.$
5. $\sin x$ has local maxima with value 1 at $x = \pi/2, 5\pi/2, 9\pi/2, \ldots,$
   so f has local maxima with value 1 when $1/x = \pi/2, 5\pi/2, 9\pi/2, \ldots$
   —that is, at $x = 2/\pi, 2/5\pi, 2/9\pi, \ldots.$

   $\sin x$ has local minima with value -1 at $x = 3\pi/2, 7\pi/2, 11\pi/2, \ldots,$
   so f has local minima with value -1 when $1/x = 3\pi/2, 7\pi/2, 11\pi/2, \ldots$
   —that is, at $x = 2/3\pi, 2/7\pi, 2/11\pi, \ldots.$

   The intervals on which f is increasing or decreasing alternate between the above stationary points.

The stationary points are ordered from right to left and become closer together as x approaches 0 from the right.

6. As $x \to \pm\infty, 1/x \to 0$ and $\sin(1/x) \to 0$. Thus the function f has a horizontal asymptote $y = 0$.
7. $-1 \leq \sin \frac{1}{x} \leq 1$, so $y = -1$ and $y = 1$ are construction lines for this graph.

This information enables us to produce the following sketch.

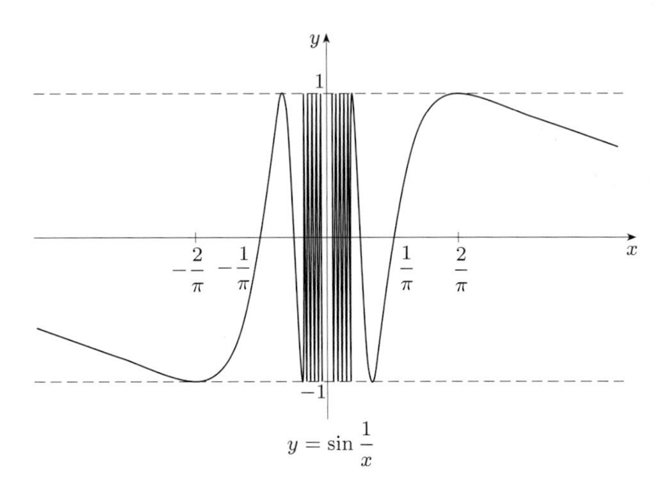

It is not possible to sketch this graph in the region close to the origin where the oscillations become closer and closer together. The function is not defined at the origin.

■

Exercise 3.3 Sketch the graph of the composite function

$$f(x) = |\sin x|.$$

We finish this subsection by looking at another function which is not defined when $x = 0$. This function is a quotient of two functions, one of which is a trigonometric function.

Example 3.3 Sketch the graph of the function

$$f(x) = \frac{\sin x}{x}.$$

Solution

1. The domain of f is $\mathbb{R}$ excluding 0; that is, it consists of the intervals $(-\infty, 0)$ and $(0, \infty)$.
2. The function f is even since $\sin(-x)/(-x) = -\sin x/-x = \sin x/x$ for $x \neq 0$. So it is sufficient initially to consider just non-negative values of x, and to reflect the graph in the y-axis to obtain the left-hand half.
3. $\frac{\sin x}{x} = 0$ when $\sin x = 0$ and $x \neq 0$.
   So the x-intercepts are $x = \pm\pi, \pm 2\pi, \pm 3\pi, \ldots$.
   There is no y-intercept, since f is not defined at $x = 0$.

0 is not an intercept, as f is not defined there.

4. When $x > 0$, f is positive on intervals where $\sin x$ is positive and negative on intervals where $\sin x$ is negative, so
   f is positive on $(0, \pi), (2\pi, 3\pi), (4\pi, 5\pi), \ldots$,
   f is negative on $(\pi, 2\pi), (3\pi, 4\pi), (5\pi, 6\pi), \ldots$.
5. $f'(x) = \frac{x \cos x - \sin x}{x^2}$, so $f'(x) = 0$ when $x \cos x - \sin x = 0$; that is, at those values of the domain where $x = \tan x$. We cannot find these values of x easily, but from the graphs of x and $\tan x$ (see below) we can see that there is one point where $x = \tan x$ in each of the intervals in step 4. So there is a maximum in each of the intervals $(0, \pi)$, $(2\pi, 3\pi)$, $(4\pi, 5\pi)$, ... where f is positive and a minimum in each of the intervals $(\pi, 2\pi)$, $(3\pi, 4\pi)$, $(5\pi, 6\pi)$, ... where f is negative.

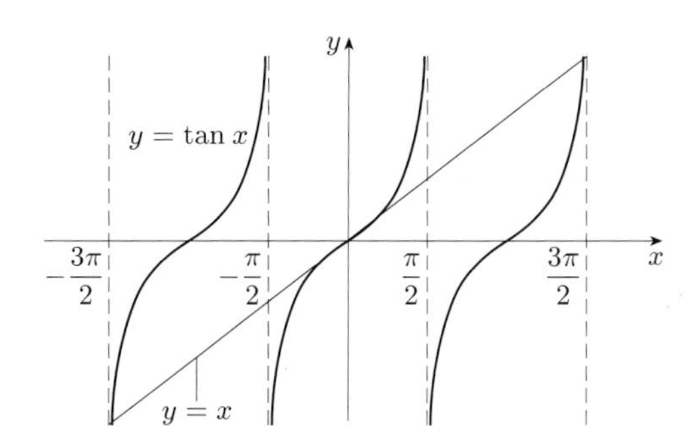

6. $f(x)$ has a horizontal asymptote $y = 0$, since $f(x) \to 0$ as $x \to \pm\infty$.
7. To finish drawing this graph we use the fact that

$$-1 \leq \sin x \leq 1, \quad \text{for all real } x.$$

So we have

$$-\frac{1}{x} \leq \frac{\sin x}{x} \leq \frac{1}{x}, \quad \text{when } x > 0$$

and

$$-\frac{1}{x} \geq \frac{\sin x}{x} \geq \frac{1}{x}, \quad \text{when } x < 0.$$

Therefore

$$-\left|\frac{1}{x}\right| \leq \frac{\sin x}{x} \leq \left|\frac{1}{x}\right|, \quad \text{for all real numbers } x.$$

So the graph of f lies between the graphs of the functions $x \longmapsto -|1/x|$ and $x \longmapsto |1/x|$. The construction lines are $y = -|1/x|$ and $y = |1/x|$.

This information enables us to produce most of the following sketch. It does not tell us, however, what happens as x approaches 0. Later in the course we shall prove that $\sin x/x \to 1$ as $x \to 0$. This allows us to complete the graph.

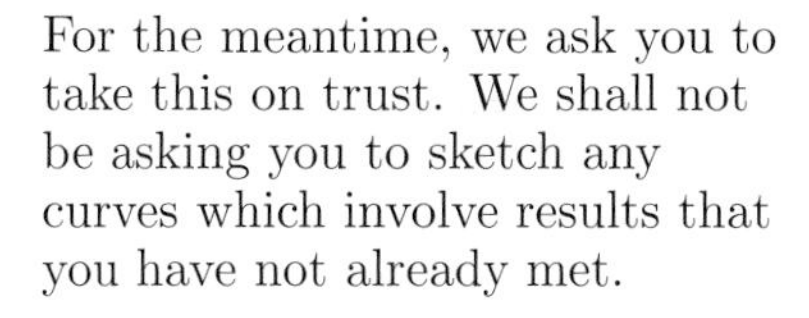
For the meantime, we ask you to take this on trust. We shall not be asking you to sketch any curves which involve results that you have not already met.

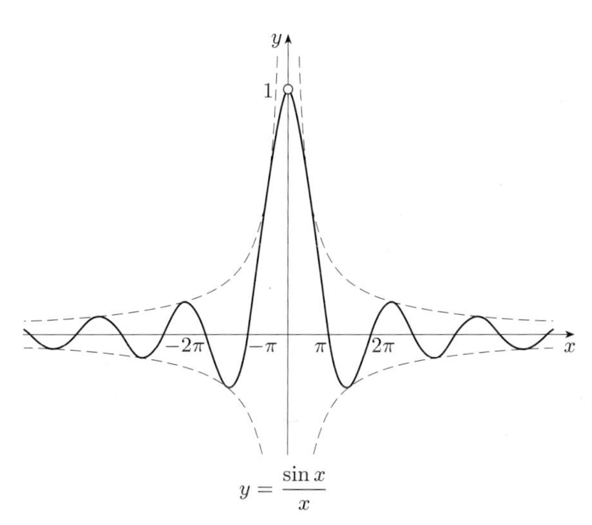

The graph has a 'hole' when $x = 0$, and it seems natural to fill this hole by defining $f(0) = 1$. We can thus extend the domain of this function to include 0.

$$g(x) = \begin{cases} \dfrac{\sin x}{x}, & x \neq 0, \\ 1, & x = 0. \end{cases}$$

This is an example of a *hybrid function*. We shall see in Analysis Block A that, with this definition, the function g is continuous at 0.

Hybrid functions are defined in the next section

However, for the function $f(x) = \sin(1/x)$ of Example 3.2, we cannot 'fill in the hole' by defining an appropriate hybrid function; whatever value we assign to $f(0)$, we cannot extend the domain of the function to the whole of $\mathbb{R}$ so that it is continuous at 0.

Informally, a function is continuous if its graph can be drawn without taking the pen off the paper.

3.2 Hybrid functions

In Section 1 we saw that the rule of a function is one of its main components. This may suggest that a function always has a single formula associated with it, but this is not the case. Some functions of the greatest practical importance have rules that are defined by different formulas on different parts of their domains—we call such functions **hybrid functions**.

For example, this text is constructed by a typesetting process called TEX which specifies each letter as a sequence of curves that join smoothly together, but are defined by several different cubic functions.

To specify a hybrid function, we need to state which rule applies on which part of the domain, and we use a curly bracket to list the different cases. For example, consider the function

$$f(x) = \begin{cases} 1, & 1 < x \le 2, \\ 0, & x \le 1 \text{ and } x > 2. \end{cases}$$

The function f has domain $\mathbb{R}$, since for each x in $\mathbb{R}$ there is a unique value of $f(x)$. It takes the value 1 on the interval $(1, 2]$, and the value 0 elsewhere, so its graph is as follows.

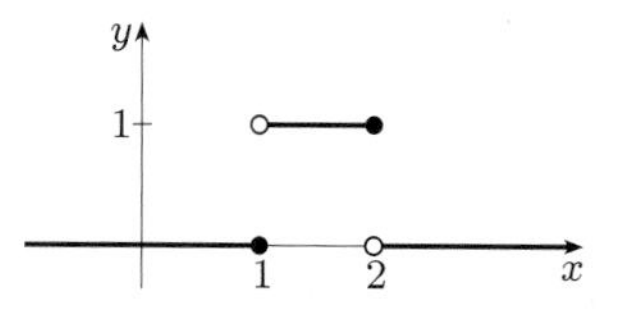

We use a solid circle • to indicate a point that belongs to the graph, and an open circle ∘ to indicate a point that does not belong to the graph.

Example 3.4 Sketch the graph of the function

$$f(x) = \begin{cases} 1 - x, & x < 0, \\ 0, & 0 \le x \le 1, \\ 3x - 3, & x > 1. \end{cases}$$

Solution The function f has domain $\mathbb{R}$.

Using our knowledge of the graphs of basic functions we can work out the graphs of the three functions

$$y = 1 - x, \quad y = 0, \quad y = 3x - 3.$$

This enables us to construct the following sketch.

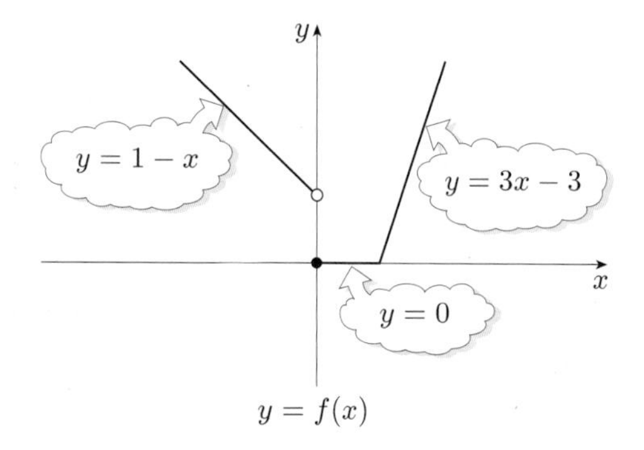

$y = f(x)$

The graph exhibits some peculiar features—a 'jump' at $x = 0$ and a 'corner' at $x = 1$. ■

The meanings of these terms will be made precise in the analysis blocks.

Exercise 3.4 Sketch the graph of each of the following hybrid functions.

(a) $f(x) = \begin{cases} x^2, & x \le 1 \\ \sqrt{x}, & x > 1 \end{cases}$ (b) $f(x) = \begin{cases} e^x, & x < 0 \\ |x-1|, & 0 \le x \le 2 \\ x-2, & x > 2 \end{cases}$

(c) $f(x) = \begin{cases} x^2, & x < 0 \\ \sin x, & x \ge 0 \end{cases}$

Further exercises

Sketch the graph of each of the following functions.

Exercise 3.5 $f(x) = 2\cos x - x$

Exercise 3.6 $f(x) = \dfrac{\cos x}{x}$

Exercise 3.7 Sketch the graph of each of the following hybrid functions.

(a) $f(x) = \begin{cases} |x|, & x \le 1 \\ -x, & x > 1 \end{cases}$ (b) $f(x) = \begin{cases} 2-x, & x < -1 \\ x^2-1, & -1 \le x \le 1 \\ \log_e x, & x > 1 \end{cases}$

4 Hyperbolic functions

After working through this section, you should be able to:

(a) define the *hyperbolic functions* $\cosh x$, $\sinh x$ and $\tanh x$, and be familiar with their properties;

(b) sketch the graphs of $\cosh x$, $\sinh x$ and $\tanh x$, and their reciprocals.

4.1 Properties of hyperbolic functions

In Subsection 1.2 you met the graph $y = e^x$ of the exponential function, often referred to as exp, which is shown in the margin. The function exp has the following properties.

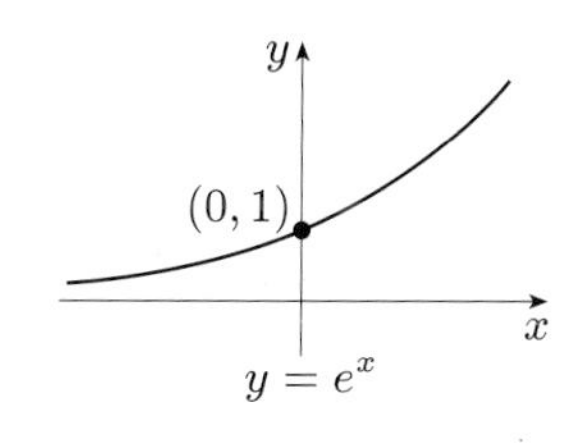

1. The domain of exp is $\mathbb{R}$.
2. exp is not even, odd or periodic.
3. $e^x > 0$ for all x in $\mathbb{R}$, so exp is positive on $\mathbb{R}$.
4. exp is its own derivative—that is, if $f(x) = e^x$, then $f'(x) = e^x$.
   Since $e^x > 0$ for all x in $\mathbb{R}$, exp is increasing on $\mathbb{R}$.
5. $e^0 = 1$, $e^x > 1$ for all $x > 0$ and $e^x < 1$ for all $x < 0$;
   $e^{x+y} = e^x \times e^y$ for all x, y in $\mathbb{R}$.
6. For each positive integer n, $e^x/x^n \to \infty$ as $x \to \infty$.
7. $e^x \to \infty$ as $x \to \infty$ and
   $e^x \to 0$ as $x \to -\infty$.

These properties are explained and discussed in greater detail in Analysis Block A.

We sometimes express property 6 by saying that e^x *grows faster than any polynomial when x is large.*

The main aim of this section is to define and explore some new functions that involve the exponential function. The following exercise gives you some practice in manipulating exponential terms.

Exercise 4.1 Simplify each of the following expressions so that it involves no products or quotients.

(a) $e^x(e^x + e^{-x})$

(b) $(e^{2x} - e^{-2x})/e^x$

(c) $(e^{5x} + e^{-5x})(e^{5x} - e^{-5x})$

Certain combinations of e^x and e^{-x} appear so frequently in mathematics that it is useful to introduce functions that involve these combinations. In this section we use the exponential function to define the hyperbolic functions sinh, cosh and tanh, all with domain $\mathbb{R}$.

The name 'hyperbolic' originates from their use as parametric forms for a hyperbola. (See Section 5.)

- cosh is the *hyperbolic cosine function*, with rule $\cosh x = \dfrac{e^x + e^{-x}}{2}$;
- sinh is the *hyperbolic sine function*, with rule $\sinh x = \dfrac{e^x - e^{-x}}{2}$;
- tanh is the *hyperbolic tangent function*, with rule $\tanh x = \dfrac{\sinh x}{\cosh x}$.

Pronounce 'cosh' as it is spelled.

Pronounce 'sinh' as 'sinsh' or 'shine'.

Pronounce 'tanh' as 'tansh' or 'than' (as in 'thank').

Although the hyperbolic functions may seem to have no connection with the trigonometric functions, the similar names arise from various properties of these functions that are similar to those of trigonometric functions.

The next two exercises demonstrate some similarities between the hyperbolic functions cosh and sinh and the trigonometric functions cos and sin.

Exercise 4.2 Using the above definitions, prove the following.

(a) $\cosh^2 x - \sinh^2 x = 1$

(b) $\cosh(x + y) = \cosh x \cosh y + \sinh x \sinh y$

(c) $\sinh(x + y) = \sinh x \cosh y + \cosh x \sinh y$

(In parts (b) and (c), start from the right-hand side.)

Here $\cosh^2 x$ and $\sinh^2 x$ are abbreviations for $(\cosh x)^2$ and $(\sinh x)^2$, respectively.

Exercise 4.3 Find the derivatives of the functions $\cosh x$ and $\sinh x$, and compare your answers with the derivatives of $\cos x$ and $\sin x$.

As you might expect, we can also define three other hyperbolic functions:

$$\operatorname{sech} x = \frac{1}{\cosh x} \quad \text{just as} \quad \sec x = \frac{1}{\cos x},$$

$$\operatorname{cosech} x = \frac{1}{\sinh x} \quad \text{just as} \quad \operatorname{cosec} x = \frac{1}{\sin x},$$

$$\coth x = \frac{1}{\tanh x} \quad \text{just as} \quad \cot x = \frac{1}{\tan x}.$$

Pronounce 'sech' as 'sesh' or 'sheck'.

Pronounce 'cosech' as 'co-sesh' or 'co-sheck'.

Pronounce 'coth' to rhyme with 'moth'.

You are now asked to investigate the properties of the function tanh.

Exercise 4.4 Let $f(x) = \tanh x$.

(a) Show that f is an odd function.

(b) Show that

$$f(x) = \frac{1 - e^{-2x}}{1 + e^{-2x}}.$$

(c) Show that $f'(x) = \operatorname{sech}^2 x$, and deduce that $f'(x) > 0$ for all x in $\mathbb{R}$.

For comparison, the derivative of tan is $\sec^2$.

The following table compares some identities satisfied by the hyperbolic functions with the corresponding identities for trigonometric functions. The hyperbolic identities are identical to the trigonometric ones, apart from a change of sign whenever a product of two sine terms occurs.

The functions tan, cosec and cot all contain a sine term.

Hyperbolic functions	**Trigonometric functions**
cosh is even: $\cosh(-x) = \cosh x$ sinh is odd: $\sinh(-x) = -\sinh x$ tanh is odd: $\tanh(-x) = -\tanh x$	cos is even: $\cos(-x) = \cos x$ sin is odd: $\sin(-x) = -\sin x$ tan is odd: $\tan(-x) = -\tan x$
$\cosh^2 x - \sinh^2 x = 1$ $1 - \tanh^2 x = \operatorname{sech}^2 x$ $\coth^2 x - 1 = \operatorname{cosech}^2 x$	$\cos^2 x + \sin^2 x = 1$ $1 + \tan^2 x = \sec^2 x$ $\cot^2 x + 1 = \operatorname{cosec}^2 x$
$\sinh(x+y) = \sinh x \cosh y + \cosh x \sinh y$ $\cosh(x+y) = \cosh x \cosh y + \sinh x \sinh y$ $\tanh(x+y) = \dfrac{\tanh x + \tanh y}{1 + \tanh x \tanh y}$	$\sin(x+y) = \sin x \cos y + \cos x \sin y$ $\cos(x+y) = \cos x \cos y - \sin x \sin y$ $\tan(x+y) = \dfrac{\tan x + \tan y}{1 - \tan x \tan y}$
$\sinh 2x = 2 \sinh x \cosh x$ $\cosh 2x = \cosh^2 x + \sinh^2 x$ $= 2\cosh^2 x - 1$ $= 1 + 2\sinh^2 x$ $\tanh 2x = \dfrac{2 \tanh x}{1 + \tanh^2 x}$	$\sin 2x = 2 \sin x \cos x$ $\cos 2x = \cos^2 x - \sin^2 x$ $= 2\cos^2 x - 1$ $= 1 - 2\sin^2 x$ $\tan 2x = \dfrac{2 \tan x}{1 - \tan^2 x}$

Finally, we ask you to use this table to obtain two further identities.

Exercise 4.5 Show that

(a) $\cosh 2x = \dfrac{1 + \tanh^2 x}{1 - \tanh^2 x}$;

(b) $\sinh 2x = \dfrac{2 \tanh x}{1 - \tanh^2 x}$.

4.2 Graphs of hyperbolic functions

We now turn our attention to sketching the graphs of the hyperbolic functions. We shall see that they bear little or no resemblance to the graphs of the corresponding trigonometric functions.

Example 4.1 Sketch the graph of the function

$f(x) = \cosh x$.

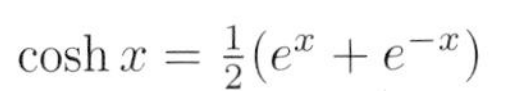

$\cosh x = \frac{1}{2}(e^x + e^{-x})$

Solution The graphs of $y = e^x$ and $y = e^{-x}$ are as follows.

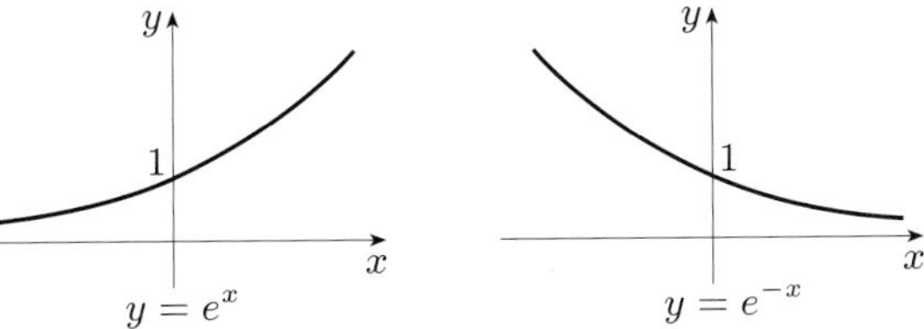
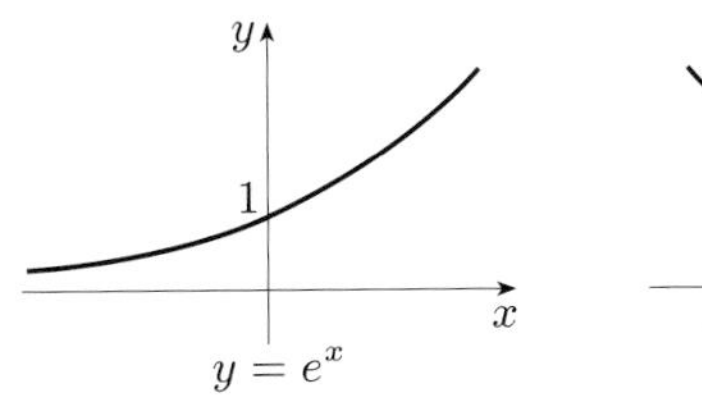

Since $\cosh x = \frac{1}{2}(e^x + e^{-x})$, we have to 'take the average' of these graphs: for each value of x, the required value is halfway between the values for these graphs.

We use Strategy 2.1.

1. $f(x) = \cosh x$ has domain $\mathbb{R}$.
2. f is even, since
$$\cosh(-x) = \frac{e^{-x} + e^{-(-x)}}{2} = \frac{e^{-x} + e^{x}}{2} = \cosh x, \quad \text{for all } x \text{ in } \mathbb{R}.$$
3. To find any x-intercepts of f we have to solve the equation
$$(e^{-x} + e^{x})/2 = 0.$$
However e^{x} and e^{-x} are positive for all x in $\mathbb{R}$, so
$$\cosh x \text{ is positive for all } x \text{ in } \mathbb{R}.$$
This means that the entire graph lies above the x-axis, so it has no x intercepts.

$f(0) = (e^{0} + e^{-0})/2 = (1 + 1)/2 = 1$, so the y-intercept is 1.
4. As shown in step 3, f is positive for all x in $\mathbb{R}$.
5. $f'(x) = \sinh x = \frac{1}{2}(e^{x} - e^{-x})$, which is positive when $x > 0$, negative when $x < 0$ and zero when $x = 0$, so

f is decreasing on the interval $(-\infty, 0)$;
f is increasing on the interval $(0, \infty)$;
f has a local minimum at 0, with value $\cosh(0) = 1$.

The graphs on page 41 illustrate the following properties:
$$e^{x} > e^{-x}, \quad \text{for } x > 0,$$
$$e^{x} < e^{-x}, \quad \text{for } x < 0.$$
We deduce that
$$\sinh x > 0, \quad \text{for } x > 0,$$
$$\sinh x < 0, \quad \text{for } x < 0.$$

6. Since $e^{x} \to \infty$ as $x \to \infty$ and $e^{-x} \to 0$ as $x \to \infty$,
$$\cosh x \to \infty \quad \text{as } x \to \infty,$$
and, since cosh is even,
$$\cosh x \to \infty \quad \text{as } x \to -\infty.$$

This information enables us to produce the following sketch.

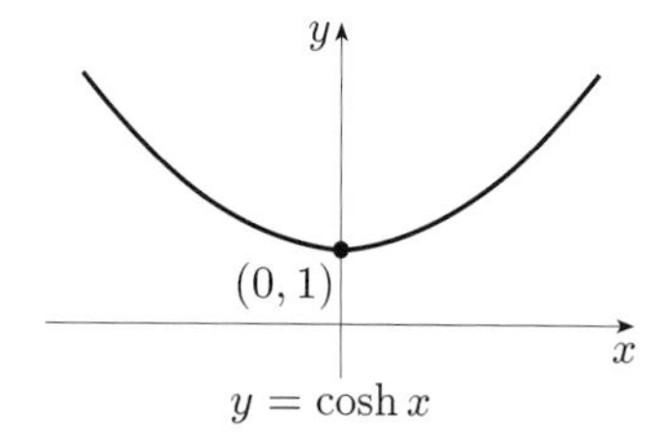

■

So the graph of the cosh function bears little resemblance to that of the cosine function; for example,
$$\cosh x \geq 1, \quad \text{for all } x \text{ in } \mathbb{R},$$
whereas
$$-1 \leq \cos x \leq 1, \quad \text{for all } x \text{ in } \mathbb{R}.$$

Nor is there much similarity between the graphs of the sinh and tanh functions and those of the sine and tangent functions, as you will discover by working through the next two exercises.

Exercise 4.6 Sketch the graph of the function
$$f(x) = \sinh x.$$

Exercise 4.7 Use the results of Exercise 4.4 to sketch the graph of the function

$$f(x) = \tanh x.$$

Using the properties of the functions cosh and sinh, we can now sketch the graphs of their reciprocals, sech and cosech.

Example 4.2 Sketch the graph of the function

$$f(x) = \operatorname{sech} x = \frac{1}{\cosh x}.$$

Solution We use Strategy 2.1.

1. f has domain $\mathbb{R}$, since $\cosh x$ is never 0.
2. f is an even function, since $\cosh x$ is an even function.
3. $\cosh x \geq 1$ for all x in $\mathbb{R}$, so

   $$0 < \operatorname{sech} x \leq 1, \quad \text{for all } x \text{ in } \mathbb{R}.$$

   So f has no x-intercepts.

   $f(0) = \operatorname{sech} 0 = \dfrac{1}{\cosh 0} = \dfrac{1}{1} = 1$. So the y-intercept is 1.
4. From step 3, f is positive for all $x \in \mathbb{R}$.
5. Since $\cosh x$ is decreasing on $(-\infty, 0)$, and increasing on $(0, \infty)$,

   $$\operatorname{sech} x \text{ is increasing on } (-\infty, 0), \text{ and decreasing on } (0, \infty);$$

   thus

   $$\operatorname{sech} x \text{ has a local maximum at 0 with value } \operatorname{sech}(0) = 1.$$
6. Since $\cosh x \to \infty$ as $x \to \pm\infty$,

   $$\operatorname{sech} x \to 0 \text{ as } x \to \pm\infty.$$

   So $y = 0$ is a horizontal asymptote.

This information enables us to produce the following sketch.

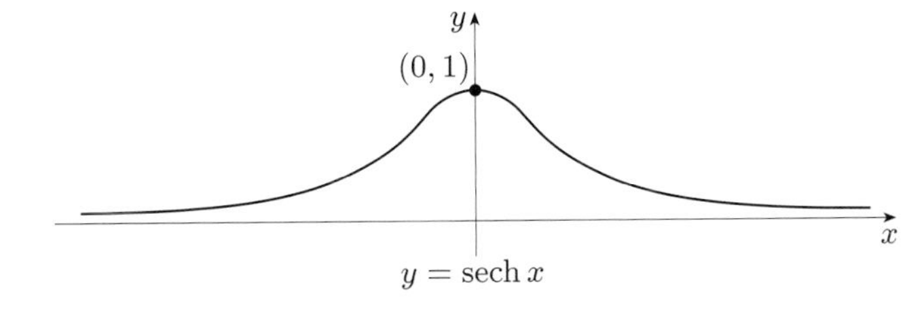

$y = \operatorname{sech} x$

■

Exercise 4.8 Sketch the graph of the function

$$f(x) = \operatorname{cosech} x.$$

Further exercises

Exercise 4.9 Prove that

$$\tanh(x + y) = \frac{\tanh x + \tanh y}{1 + \tanh x \tanh y}.$$

Exercise 4.10 Sketch the graph of the function $f(x) = \coth x$.

5 Curves from parameters

After working through this section, you should be able to:

(a) plot a curve that is specified by a *parametric* representation;

(b) obtain the equation of a curve that is specified by a parametric representation, in simple cases;

(c) sketch a conic whose equation is given in standard form.

5.1 Parametric equations

Suppose that you are wheeling a bicycle along a flat road. There is a piece of mud on the outside of one of the tyres. What curve does the piece of mud trace out as the bicycle moves?

Intuitively, we expect to obtain some sort of arch, such as the following, but what is its equation?

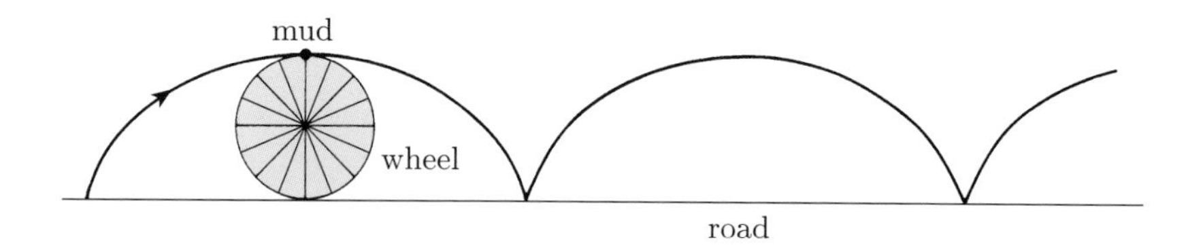

Such a curve is called a **cycloid**. Unfortunately, there is no simple formula that directly expresses the vertical coordinate y of a point on the cycloid in terms of the horizontal coordinate x. However, if we track the position of the mud at each moment of time, we can obtain x and y as functions of the time t taken to reach the point (x, y).

We assume for simplicity that the wheel has radius 1 and that the bicycle is being wheeled at a rate of 1 radian per second. Also, when $t = 0$, the mud is at the origin in the diagram. Then the time t (in seconds) is equal to the angle (in radians) between the radius from the mud to the wheel centre and the radius from the road to the wheel centre. From the diagram in the margin, we have

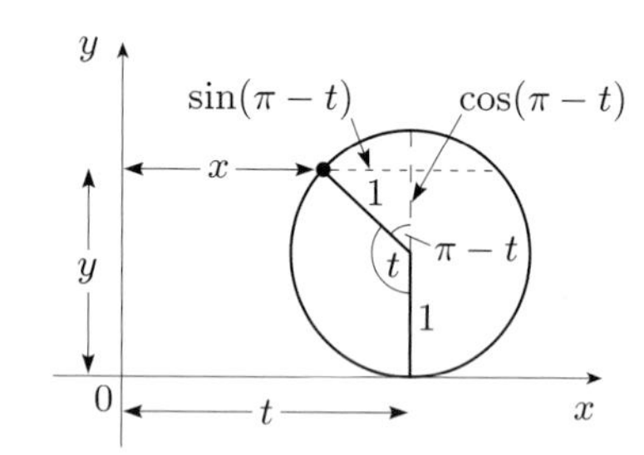

$$x = t - \sin(\pi - t) = t - \sin t,$$
$$y = 1 + \cos(\pi - t) = 1 - \cos t.$$

Thus, the coordinates (x, y) of the mud after t seconds are given by the pair of equations

$$x = t - \sin t, \quad y = 1 - \cos t. \tag{5.1}$$

Using these equations, we can calculate the position of the mud at any given time, and draw up a table of approximate function values for the first revolution; for example, it follows from equations (5.1) that when $t = 4\pi/3$,

$$x = 4\pi/3 - \sin(4\pi/3) = 4\pi/3 - (-\sqrt{3}/2) \simeq 5.055,$$
$$y = 1 - \cos(4\pi/3) = 1 - (-1/2) = 1.5.$$

We thus obtain the following table.

Time t	0	$\pi/3$	$2\pi/3$	π	$4\pi/3$	$5\pi/3$	2π
Horizontal distance x	0	0.181	1.228	3.142	5.055	6.102	6.283
Vertical distance y	0	0.500	1.500	2.000	1.500	0.500	0

These points are indicated on the cycloid below.

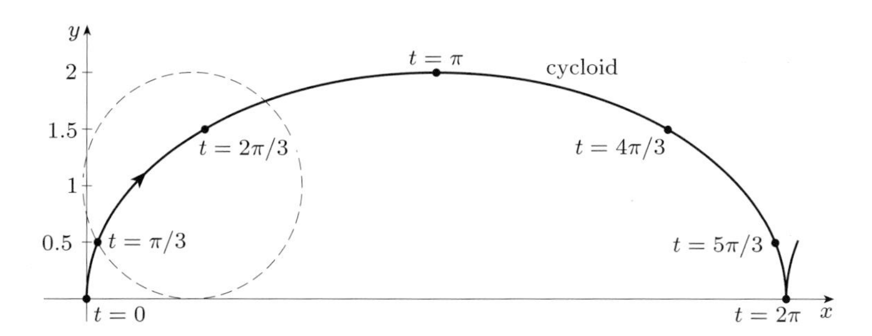

Exercise 5.1 Verify the values of x and y in the table when $t = \pi/3$ and $t = \pi$, and calculate the points on the curve corresponding to $t = \pi/2$ and $t = \pi/6$.

We call the above pair of equations (5.1), giving the values of x and y in terms of t, *parametric equations* for the cycloid, and the variable t is called the *parameter*.

In general, **parametric equations** for a curve have the form

$$x = f(t), \quad y = g(t),$$

where f and g are real functions of the **parameter** t. Both f and g have the same domain, which is usually an interval I of the real line; for a single arch of the cycloid, an appropriate interval is $[0, 2\pi]$, as we saw above.

Moreover, we can use the functions f and g to define a new function α, whose domain is the interval I and whose rule is $t \longmapsto (f(t), g(t))$, where $t \in I$; the codomain of this function is usually taken to be the Cartesian xy-plane $\mathbb{R}^2$.

As the parameter t moves along the interval I, the image point

$$\alpha(t) = (f(t), g(t)), \quad \text{for } t \text{ in } I,$$

moves along a curve in the codomain $\mathbb{R}^2$.

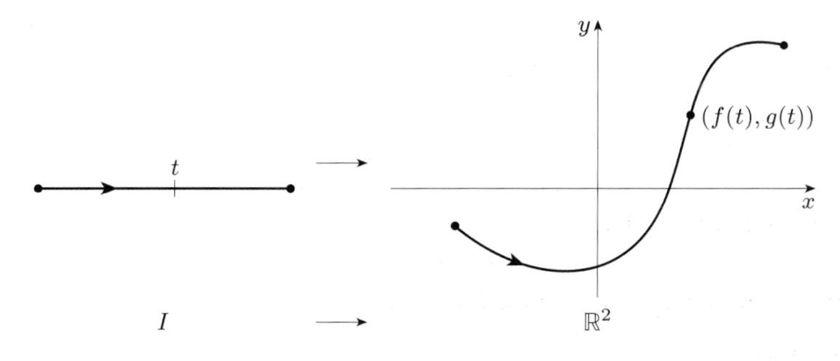

The function α is called a **parametrisation** of the curve in $\mathbb{R}^2$. For example, the function α defined by

$$\alpha(t) = (t - \sin t, 1 - \cos t), \quad \text{for } t \text{ in } [0, 2\pi],$$

is a parametrisation of an arch of the cycloid (see the following diagram).

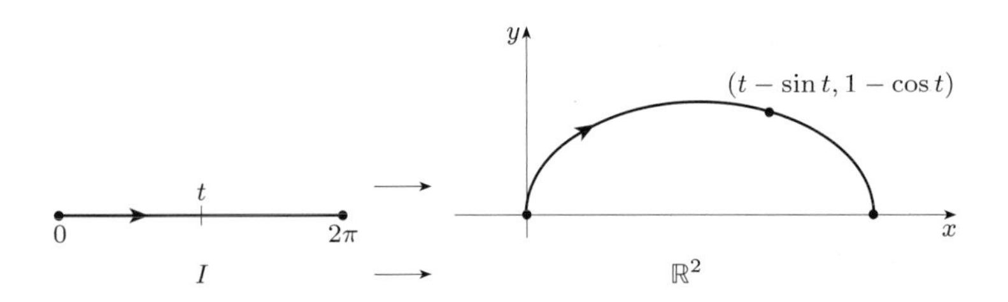

5.2 Parametrising conics and other curves

We have seen that parametric equations can be useful for specifying certain curves when there is no simple formula relating the coordinates x and y. They are also useful when the curve in question is not the graph of a function.

To see what we mean, consider the unit circle with equation $x^2 + y^2 = 1$. For a *function*, each value of x must give rise to a *unique* value of y, but here this is not the case; for example, when $x = 0$, then y can be either 1 or -1.

We can avoid this problem by the use of parametric equations.

Parametrising circles

In the diagram in the margin, (x, y) denotes a general point on the unit circle. We can express x and y in terms of the angle t (measured anticlockwise from the positive real axis) by the equations

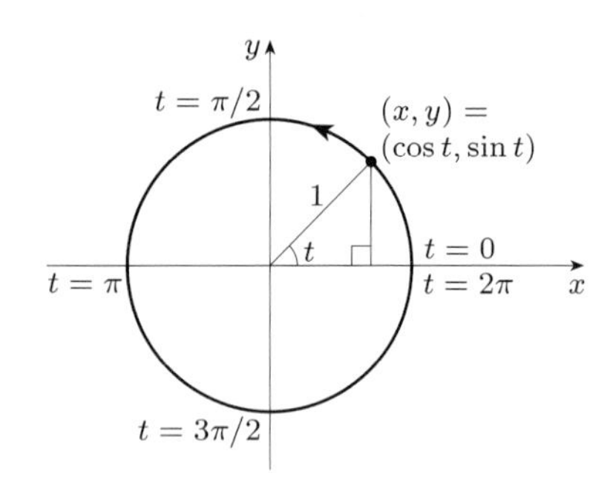

$$x = \cos t, \quad y = \sin t. \tag{5.2}$$

As the angle t increases from 0 to 2π, the point (x, y) travels once round the circle anticlockwise, starting and ending at the point $(1, 0)$.

In the language of the previous subsection, t is a *parameter* and equations (5.2) are *parametric equations* for the unit circle, giving rise to the *parametrisation*

$$\alpha(t) = (\cos t, \sin t), \quad \text{for } t \text{ in } [0, 2\pi].$$

In this case, we can use the trigonometric identity

$$\cos^2 t + \sin^2 t = 1$$

to eliminate the parameter t from equations (5.2) and obtain the equation $x^2 + y^2 = 1$, as expected.

Exercise 5.2 Mark on a unit circle the coordinates of the points that correspond to the following values of the parameter t:

$$t = \pi/6, \quad t = \pi/2, \quad t = 3\pi/4, \quad t = \pi, \quad t = 3\pi/2, \quad t = 5\pi/3.$$

Similarly, we can write down a parametrisation for a circle of any radius, centred at the origin. Such a circle has equation $x^2 + y^2 = a^2$, where a is the radius of the circle.

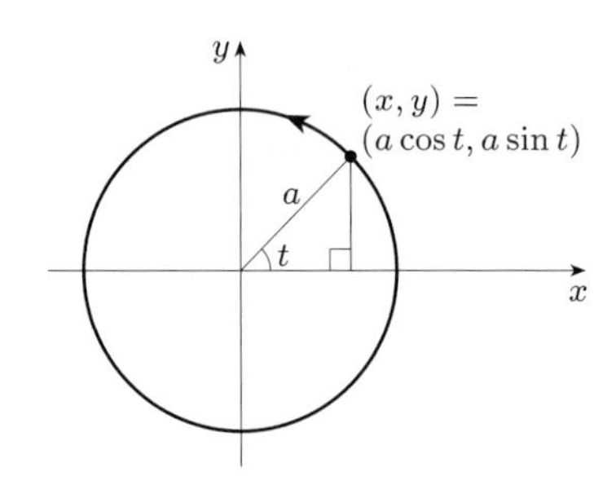

For this circle, we use the parametrisation

$$\alpha(t) = (a \cos t, a \sin t), \quad \text{for } t \text{ in } [0, 2\pi];$$

this corresponds to the parametric equations

$$x = a \cos t, \quad y = a \sin t.$$

In this case, we can eliminate the parameter t by writing $x/a = \cos t$ and $y/a = \sin t$, and using the trigonometric identity $\cos^2 t + \sin^2 t = 1$; this gives the equation $x^2 + y^2 = a^2$, as expected.

Exercise 5.3 Write down a parametrisation for each of the following:

(a) the circle centred at the origin, with radius 3;

(b) the circle with centre $(2, 1)$ and radius 3.

Exercise 5.4 Show that another parametrisation for the unit circle is

$$x = \cos 2\pi t, \quad y = \sin 2\pi t, \quad \text{for } t \text{ in } [0, 1].$$

We now have two different parametrisations for the unit circle traversed once anticlockwise—namely

$$\alpha(t) = (\cos t, \sin t), \quad \text{for } t \text{ in } [0, 2\pi],$$

and

$$\alpha(t) = (\cos 2\pi t, \sin 2\pi t), \quad \text{for } t \text{ in } [0, 1].$$

This illustrates the important fact that a parametrisation of a given curve is not unique. Different parametrisations of a curve may correspond to different modes of traversing the curve.

Parametrising lines

The line through the points $(0, 0)$ and (p, q), where at least one of p, q is not zero, has equation

$$py = qx;$$

or, when $p \neq 0$,

$$y = (q/p)x.$$

For this line, we use the parametrisation

$$\alpha(t) = (pt, qt), \quad \text{for } t \text{ in } \mathbb{R};$$

this corresponds to the parametric equations

$$x = pt, \quad y = qt.$$

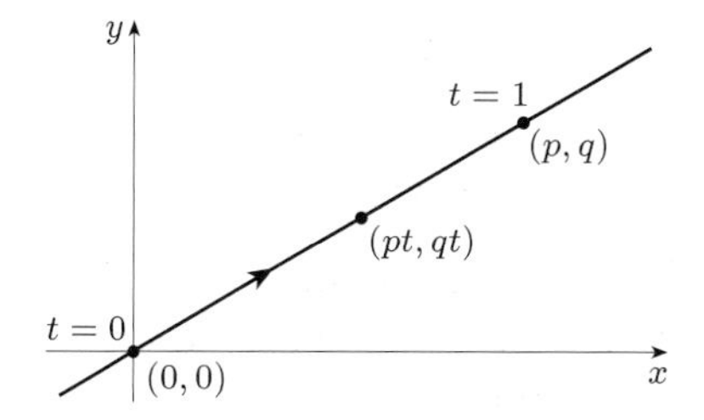

The line segment between the two given points corresponds to values of t between 0 and 1.

When $p \neq 0$, we can eliminate the parameter t by writing

$$y = \frac{q}{p} pt = \frac{q}{p} x;$$

this gives the equation $y = (q/p)x$, as expected.

When $p = 0$, the parametric equations become

$$x = 0, \quad y = qt,$$

giving the equation $x = 0$.

More generally, the line through the points (p, q) and (r, s), where $r \neq p$, has equation

$$y - q = \frac{s - q}{r - p}(x - p).$$

For this line, we use the parametrisation

$$\alpha(t) = (p + (r - p)t, q + (s - q)t), \quad \text{for } t \text{ in } \mathbb{R};$$

this gives the parametric equations

$$x = p + (r - p)t, \quad y = q + (s - q)t.$$

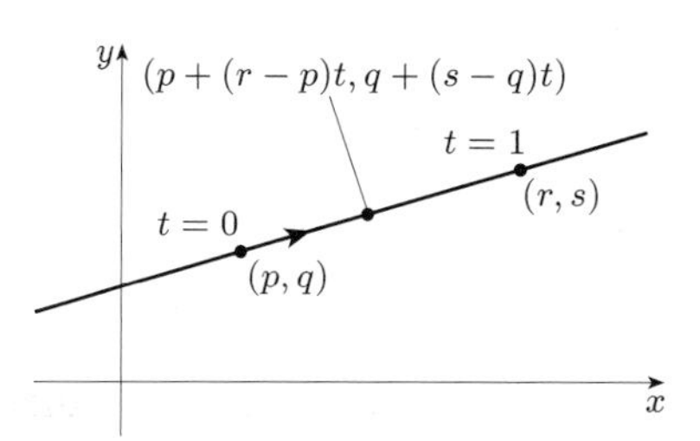

We can eliminate the parameter t to retrieve the equation of the line; we omit the details.

Exercise 5.5

(a) Write down a parametrisation for the line through the points $(1, 2)$ and $(3, 6)$.

(b) Which values of the parameter t correspond to the points $(2, 4)$, $(7, 14)$ and $(0, 0)$?

Exercise 5.6 Show that we can also parametrise the line through the points $(0, 0)$ and (p, q), where $p \neq 0$, by using the parametric equations

$$x = pt^3, \quad y = qt^3.$$

Parametrising conics

The curves that can be obtained by cutting a plane section through a cone are called *conic sections* or *conics*.

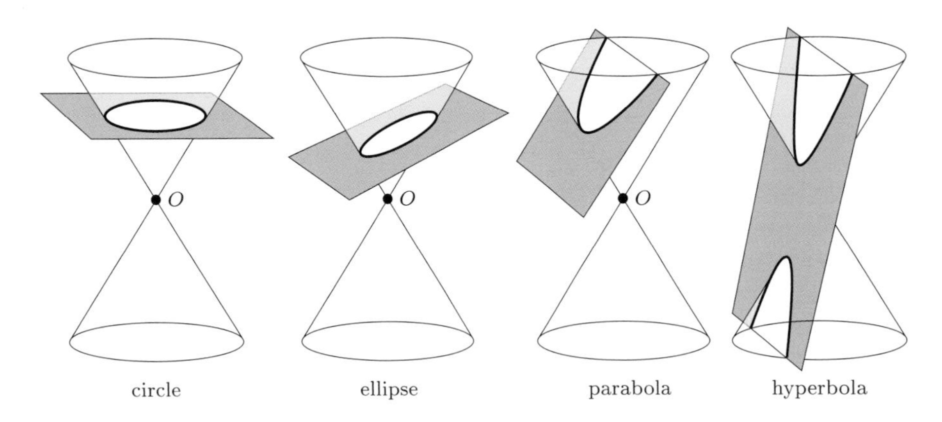

These curves are of three types:

- ellipses,
- parabolas,
- hyperbolas.

Here we present the standard and parametric forms of the equations of these *non-degenerate* conics, together with their main features.

If the plane section passes through the origin, it can also produce a point, a single line and a pair of lines. These are called *degenerate* conics.

A circle is a special case of an ellipse.

Ellipse

The equation of an **ellipse** in standard form is

$$\frac{x^2}{a^2} + \frac{y^2}{b^2} = 1, \quad \text{where } a \geq b > 0.$$

When $b = a$, the equation reduces to that of the circle centred at the origin, with radius a, discussed above.

The ellipse has centre $(0, 0)$ and crosses the axes at the points $(a, 0)$, $(0, b)$, $(-a, 0)$ and $(0, -b)$.

It is unchanged under a rotation through π about the origin, or under a reflection in either of the coordinate axes.

For the ellipse, we use the parametrisation

$$\alpha(t) = (a \cos t, b \sin t), \quad \text{for } t \text{ in } [0, 2\pi];$$

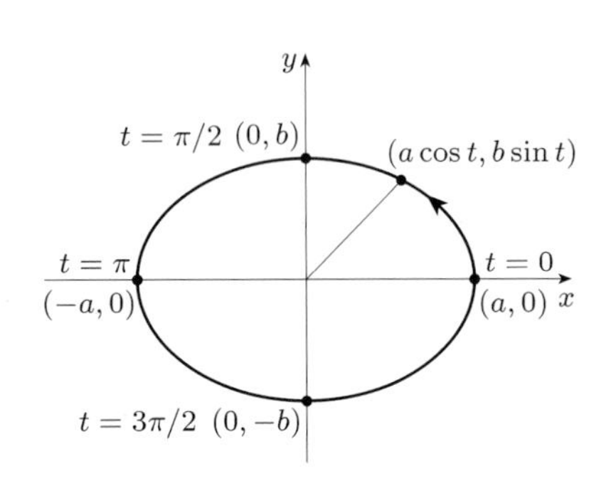

this gives the parametric equations

$$x = a \cos t, \quad y = b \sin t.$$

In this case, we can eliminate the parameter t by writing

$$\frac{x}{a} = \cos t, \quad \frac{y}{b} = \sin t,$$

and using the trigonometric identity $\cos^2 t + \sin^2 t = 1$.

This gives the equation

$$\frac{x^2}{a^2} + \frac{y^2}{b^2} = 1,$$

as expected.

Parabola

The equation of a **parabola** in standard form is

$$y^2 = 4ax, \quad \text{where } a > 0.$$

The vertex of the parabola is at $(0, 0)$.

The parabola is unchanged under a reflection in the x-axis.

For the parabola, we use the parametrisation

$$\alpha(t) = (at^2, 2at), \quad \text{for } t \text{ in } \mathbb{R};$$

this gives the parametric equations

$$x = at^2, \quad y = 2at.$$

In this case, we can eliminate the parameter t by writing

$$y^2 = (2at)^2 = 4a^2t^2 = 4a \times at^2 = 4ax;$$

this gives $y^2 = 4ax$, as expected.

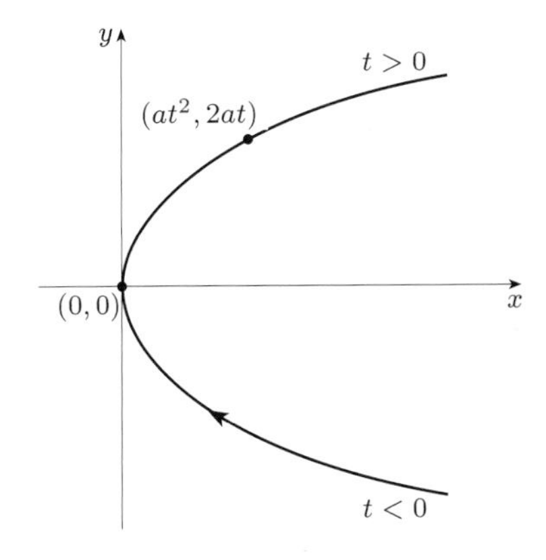

Hyperbola

The equation of a **hyperbola** in standard form is

$$\frac{x^2}{a^2} - \frac{y^2}{b^2} = 1, \quad \text{where } a > 0 \text{ and } b > 0.$$

The hyperbola has centre $(0, 0)$ and crosses the x-axis at the points $(a, 0)$ and $(-a, 0)$.

It is unchanged under a rotation through π about the origin, or under a reflection in either of the coordinate axes.

For the hyperbola, we use the parametrisation

$$\alpha(t) = (a \sec t, b \tan t), \quad \text{for } t \text{ in } [-\pi, \pi], \text{ excluding } -\pi/2 \text{ and } \pi/2;$$

this gives the parametric equations

$$x = a \sec t, \quad y = b \tan t.$$

In this case, we can eliminate the parameter t by writing

$$\frac{x}{a} = \sec t, \quad \frac{y}{b} = \tan t,$$

and using the trigonometric identity $\sec^2 t - \tan^2 t = 1$; this gives the equation

$$\frac{x^2}{a^2} - \frac{y^2}{b^2} = 1,$$

as expected.

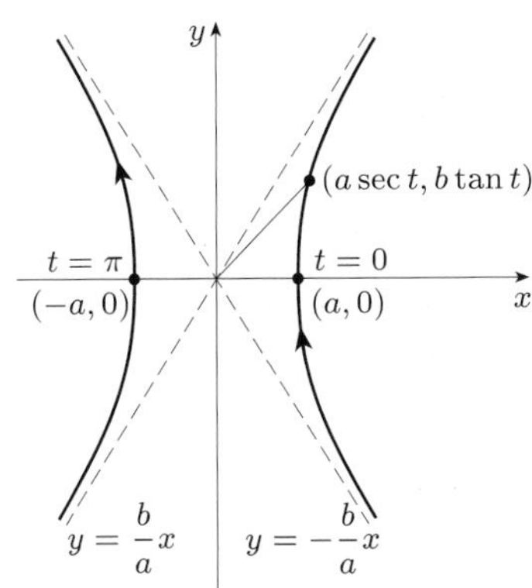

The lines $y = (b/a)x$ and $y = -(b/a)x$ are both asymptotes for the hyperbola. The asymptotes help us to sketch the graph of the hyperbola in the correct position, as described in Sections 1 and 2.

Exercise 5.7 Using the information given above, sketch the following conics.

(a) $y^2 = 2x$ (b) $\dfrac{x^2}{3} + \dfrac{y^2}{2} = 1$ (c) $\dfrac{x^2}{3} - \dfrac{y^2}{2} = 1$

Write down a parametrisation for each conic.

Exercise 5.8 Show that points on the curve with parametrisation

$$\alpha(t) = (a\cosh t, b\sinh t), \quad \text{for } t \text{ in } \mathbb{R},$$

lie on the right-hand half of the hyperbola $\dfrac{x^2}{a^2} - \dfrac{y^2}{b^2} = 1$.

This gives another parametrisation for the hyperbola. However, since $a\cosh t > 0$, we obtain only the right-hand half of the hyperbola (corresponding to $x > 0$).

In the following table we summarise the standard parametrisations for lines and conics.

Line through (p,q) and (r,s) $y - q = \dfrac{s-q}{r-p}(x-p)$	$\alpha(t) = (p + (r-p)t, q + (s-q)t)$, for t in $\mathbb{R}$	y; (p,q); (r,s); x
Circle centre $(0,0)$, radius a $x^2 + y^2 = a^2$	$\alpha(t) = (a\cos t, a\sin t)$, for t in $[0, 2\pi]$	y; a; $-a$; a; x; $-a$
Ellipse in standard form $\dfrac{x^2}{a^2} + \dfrac{y^2}{b^2} = 1$	$\alpha(t) = (a\cos t, b\sin t)$, for t in $[0, 2\pi]$	y; b; $-a$; a; x; $-b$
Parabola in standard form $y^2 = 4ax$	$\alpha(t) = (at^2, 2at)$, for t in $\mathbb{R}$	y; a; x
Hyperbola in standard form $\dfrac{x^2}{a^2} - \dfrac{y^2}{b^2} = 1$	$\alpha(t) = (a\sec t, b\tan t)$, for t in $[-\pi, \pi]$, excluding $-\pi/2$ and $\pi/2$ or $\alpha(t) = (a\cosh t, b\sinh t)$, for t in $\mathbb{R}$ (right-hand half only)	y; $y = -\frac{b}{a}x$; $-a$; a; x; $y = \frac{b}{a}x$

Finally, we give the standard parametrisation for two, more exotic, curves.

For each of these curves, it is possible, with some effort, to eliminate the parameter t to obtain a single equation involving x and y that is satisfied by all points on the curve; for example, all the points on the cardioid satisfy a polynomial equation in x and y of degree 4. However, the parametric equations for these curves are much more useful, and for many other curves no single equation can be found.

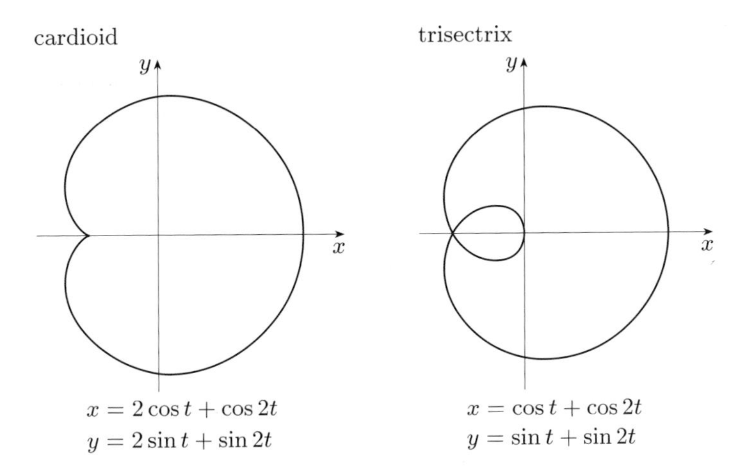

$x = 2\cos t + \cos 2t$
$y = 2\sin t + \sin 2t$

$x = \cos t + \cos 2t$
$y = \sin t + \sin 2t$

Further exercises

Exercise 5.9 Identify the curves described by the following parametric equations.

(a) $x = t, \quad y = 1/t$.

(b) $x = t - 1, \quad y = 4 - 3t$.

(c) $x = 2t, \quad y = 1 + 3t^2$.

Exercise 5.10 Consider the parametrisation

$$\alpha(t) = (2\cos t + \cos 2t,\ 2\sin t + \sin 2t).$$

(a) Calculate

$$\alpha(0), \quad \alpha(\tfrac{1}{6}\pi), \quad \alpha(\tfrac{1}{3}\pi), \quad \alpha(\tfrac{1}{2}\pi), \quad \alpha(\tfrac{2}{3}\pi), \quad \alpha(\tfrac{5}{6}\pi), \quad \alpha(\pi).$$

(b) Show that

the function $f(t) = 2\cos t + \cos 2t$ is even,
the function $g(t) = 2\sin t + \sin 2t$ is odd.

What can you deduce about the curve with parametrisation $\alpha(t)$?

(c) Use parts (a) and (b) to sketch the curve with parametrisation $\alpha(t)$.

Solutions to the exercises

1.1 (a) The denominator of $f(x)$ is $1 - x^2$, which is zero when $x = 1$ and -1, so the domain is the set of all real numbers, excluding 1 and -1.

(b) This function is defined for all real numbers, so the domain is $\mathbb{R}$.

(c) The denominator of $f(x)$ is $x^2 + 5x + 4 = (x+1)(x+4)$, which is zero when $x = -1$ and -4, so the domain is the set of all real numbers, excluding -1 and -4.

(d) The denominator of $f(x)$ is $\sqrt{1-x^2}$, which is zero when $x = 1$ and -1, and is not defined when $x^2 > 1$, that is, when $x > 1$ and $x < -1$, so the domain is the set of all real numbers strictly between -1 and 1.

1.2 (a) $(-\infty, -1)$, $(-1, 1)$, $(1, \infty)$

(b) $\mathbb{R} = (-\infty, \infty)$

(c) $(-\infty, -4)$, $(-4, -1)$, $(-1, \infty)$

(d) $(-1, 1)$

2.1 (a) In this case $a = 1$, so

$$\begin{aligned} x^2 - 6x + 11 &= (x^2 - 6x) + 11 \\ &= (x-3)^2 - 9 + 11 \\ &= (x-3)^2 + 2 \end{aligned}$$

which is always positive.

(b) In this case $a = 3$, so

$$\begin{aligned} 3x^2 + 12x - 1 &= 3(x^2 + 4x) - 1 \\ &= 3(x+2)^2 - 12 - 1 \\ &= 3(x+2)^2 - 13 \end{aligned}$$

which is sometimes positive and sometimes negative (for example, positive when $x = 1$ and negative when $x = 0$).

2.2 $f(x) \to 0$ as $x \to -\infty$;
$f(x) \to 0$ as $x \to \infty$;
$f(x) \to \infty$ as $x \to 1^-$;
$f(x) \to -\infty$ as $x \to 1^+$.

2.3 (a) $f(x) \to \infty$ as $x \to \infty$;
$f(x) \to \infty$ as $x \to -\infty$.

(b) $f(x) \to \infty$ as $x \to \infty$;
$f(x) \to -\infty$ as $x \to -\infty$.

(c) $f(x) \to -\infty$ as $x \to \infty$;
$f(x) \to -\infty$ as $x \to -\infty$.

(d) $f(x) \to -\infty$ as $x \to \infty$;
$f(x) \to \infty$ as $x \to -\infty$.

2.4 $f(x) = x^4 - 2x^2 + 3$.

1. The domain of f is $\mathbb{R}$.

2. f is even, since, for all x in $\mathbb{R}$,
$$\begin{aligned} f(-x) &= (-x)^4 - 2(-x)^2 + 3 \\ &= x^4 - 2x^2 + 3 = f(x). \end{aligned}$$

3. Using the hint to complete the square shows that $f(x) = (x^2-1)^2 + 2 \geq 2$ for all x in $\mathbb{R}$, so f is positive on $\mathbb{R}$. This means that f has no x-intercepts, as $f(x)$ is never zero. The y-intercept is $f(0) = 3$.

4. By step 3, f is positive on $\mathbb{R}$.

5. $$\begin{aligned} f'(x) &= 4x^3 - 4x \\ &= 4x(x^2 - 1) \\ &= 4x(x-1)(x+1). \end{aligned}$$

We construct a sign table for $f'(x)$.

x	$(-\infty, -1)$	-1	$(-1, 0)$	0	$(0, 1)$	1	$(1, \infty)$
$4x$	$-$	$-$	$-$	0	$+$	$+$	$+$
$x-1$	$-$	$-$	$-$	$-$	$-$	0	$+$
$x+1$	$-$	0	$+$	$+$	$+$	$+$	$+$
$f'(x)$	$-$	0	$+$	0	$-$	0	$+$

From the table, we find that

f is increasing on the intervals $(-1, 0)$ and $(1, \infty)$;

f is decreasing on the intervals $(-\infty, -1)$ and $(0, 1)$;

$f'(x) = 0$ when $x = -1$, 0 and 1.

So

f has stationary points at $x = -1, 0$ and 1.

We deduce that

there is a local minimum at $x = -1$ with $f(-1) = 2$;

there is a local maximum at $x = 0$ with $f(0) = 3$;

there is a local minimum at $x = 1$ with $f(1) = 2$.

6. The polynomial has degree 4 (even), and the coefficient of x^4 is positive, so

$f(x) \to \infty$ as $x \to \infty$,

$f(x) \to \infty$ as $x \to -\infty$.

This information enables us to sketch the graph.

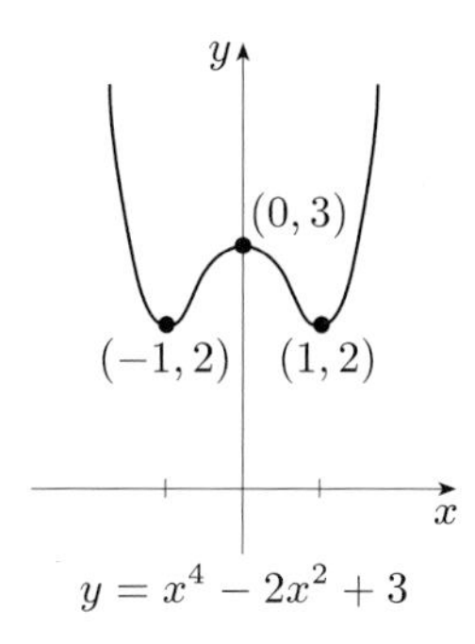

2.5 $f(x) = \dfrac{x-3}{2-x}$.

1. The domain of f is $\mathbb{R}$, excluding 2.

2. f is neither even nor odd, since its domain is not symmetric about the origin.

3. $f(x) = 0$ only when $x = 3$, so the only x-intercept is 3.

The y-intercept is $f(0) = -\frac{3}{2}$.

4. We construct a sign table for $f(x)$.

x	$(-\infty, 2)$	2	$(2, 3)$	3	$(3, \infty)$
$x-3$	$-$	$-$	$-$	0	$+$
$2-x$	$+$	0	$-$	$-$	$-$
$f(x)$	$-$	*	$+$	0	$-$

Thus

f is positive on the interval $(2, 3)$;

f is negative on the intervals $(-\infty, 2)$ and $(3, \infty)$.

5. $f'(x) = \dfrac{(2-x)+(x-3)}{(2-x)^2} = \dfrac{-1}{(2-x)^2}$,

so $f'(x) < 0$ for all x in the domain; that is, f is decreasing on each interval of its domain.

6. The denominator is 0 when $x = 2$, so

the line $x = 2$ is a vertical asymptote.

Also, by step 4,

$f(x) \to -\infty$ as $x \to 2^-$,

$f(x) \to \infty$ as $x \to 2^+$.

Dividing both numerator and denominator of $f(x)$ by x, we obtain

$$f(x) = \frac{1 - 3/x}{2/x - 1} \to \frac{1-0}{0-1} = -1 \quad \text{as } x \to \pm\infty,$$

so

the line $y = -1$ is a horizontal asymptote.

This information enables us to sketch the graph.

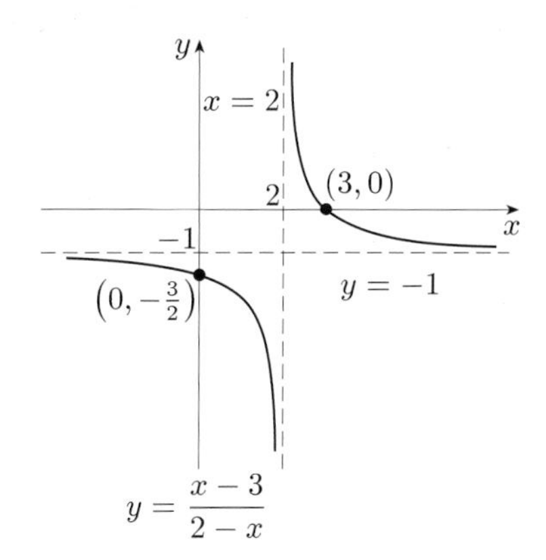

2.6 $f(x) = \dfrac{4x+1}{3x-5}$.

1. The domain of f is $\mathbb{R}$, excluding $\frac{5}{3}$.

2. f is neither even nor odd, since its domain is not symmetric about the origin.

3. $f(x) = 0$ when $x = -\frac{1}{4}$, so the x-intercept is $-\frac{1}{4}$.
The y-intercept is $f(0) = -\frac{1}{5}$.

4. We construct a sign table for $f(x)$.

x	$(-\infty, -\frac{1}{4})$	$-\frac{1}{4}$	$(-\frac{1}{4}, \frac{5}{3})$	$\frac{5}{3}$	$(\frac{5}{3}, \infty)$
$4x+1$	$-$	0	$+$	$+$	$+$
$3x-5$	$-$	$-$	$-$	0	$+$
$f(x)$	$+$	0	$-$	*	$+$

Thus

f is positive on the intervals $(-\infty, -\frac{1}{4})$ and $(\frac{5}{3}, \infty)$;

f is negative on the interval $(-\frac{1}{4}, \frac{5}{3})$.

5. $f'(x) = \dfrac{(3x-5)4 - (4x+1)3}{(3x-5)^2} = \dfrac{-23}{(3x-5)^2}$,

so $f'(x) < 0$ for all x in the domain; that is, f is decreasing on each interval of its domain.

6. The denominator is 0 when $x = \frac{5}{3}$, so

the line $x = \frac{5}{3}$ is a vertical asymptote.

Also, by step 4,

$f(x) \to -\infty$ as $x \to \frac{5}{3}^-$,

$f(x) \to \infty$ as $x \to \frac{5}{3}^+$.

Dividing both numerator and denominator of $f(x)$ by x, we obtain

$$f(x) = \frac{4 + 1/x}{3 - 5/x} \to \frac{4}{3} \quad \text{as } x \to \pm\infty,$$

so

the line $y = \frac{4}{3}$ is a horizontal asymptote.

This information enables us to sketch the graph.

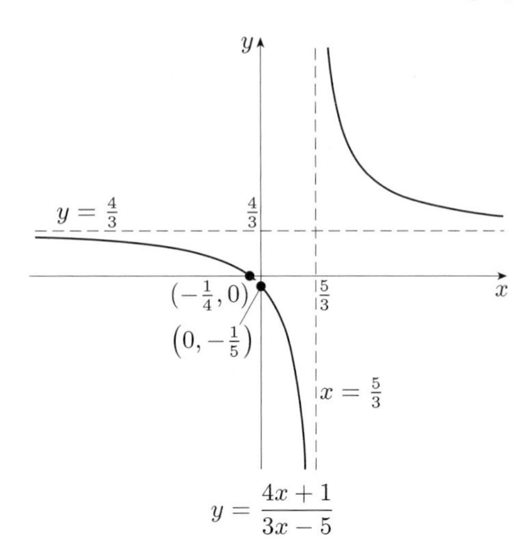

2.7 $f(x) = \dfrac{1}{x(x+1)^2}$.

1. The domain of f is $\mathbb{R}$, excluding 0 and -1; it consists of the intervals $(-\infty, -1)$, $(-1, 0)$ and $(0, \infty)$.

2. f is neither even nor odd, since the domain is not symmetric about the origin.

3. f has no x-intercepts.

$f(0)$ is not defined, so there is no y-intercept.

4. We construct a sign table for f.

x	$(\infty, -1)$	-1	$(-1, 0)$	0	$(0, \infty)$
x	$-$	$-$	$-$	0	$+$
$(x+1)^2$	$+$	0	$+$	$+$	$+$
$f(x)$	$-$	$*$	$-$	$*$	$+$

Thus

f is positive on the interval $(0, \infty)$;

f is negative on the intervals $(-\infty, -1)$ and $(-1, 0)$.

5. $$f'(x) = -\frac{(x+1)^2 + 2x(x+1)}{x^2(x+1)^4} = -\frac{(x+1)(x+1+2x)}{x^2(x+1)^4} = -\frac{3x+1}{x^2(x+1)^3},$$

so

$f'(x) = 0$ when $x = -\frac{1}{3}$.

We construct a sign table for $f'(x)$.

x		-1	$(-1, -\frac{1}{3})$	$-\frac{1}{3}$	$(-\frac{1}{3}, 0)$	0	
$-(3x+1)$	$+$	$+$	$+$	0	$-$	$-$	$-$
x^2	$+$	$+$	$+$	$+$	$+$	0	$+$
$(x+1)^3$	$-$	0	$+$	$+$	$+$	$+$	$+$
$f'(x)$	$-$	$*$	$+$	0	$-$	$*$	$-$

We deduce that

f is increasing on the interval $(-1, -\frac{1}{3})$;

f is decreasing on the intervals $(-\infty, -1)$, $(-\frac{1}{3}, 0)$ and $(0, \infty)$;

f has a stationary point at $x = -\frac{1}{3}$.

The point $x = -\frac{1}{3}$ is a local maximum with $f(-\frac{1}{3}) = -\frac{27}{4}$.

6. The denominator is 0 when $x = 0$ or $x = -1$, so

the lines $x = 0$ and $x = -1$ are vertical asymptotes.

Also, by step 4,

$f(x) \to -\infty$ as $x \to -1^-$,
$f(x) \to -\infty$ as $x \to -1^+$;
$f(x) \to -\infty$ as $x \to 0^-$,
$f(x) \to \infty$ as $x \to 0^+$.

Also,

$f(x) \to 0$ as $x \to \pm\infty$,

so

the line $y = 0$ is a horizontal asymptote.

This information enables us to sketch the graph.

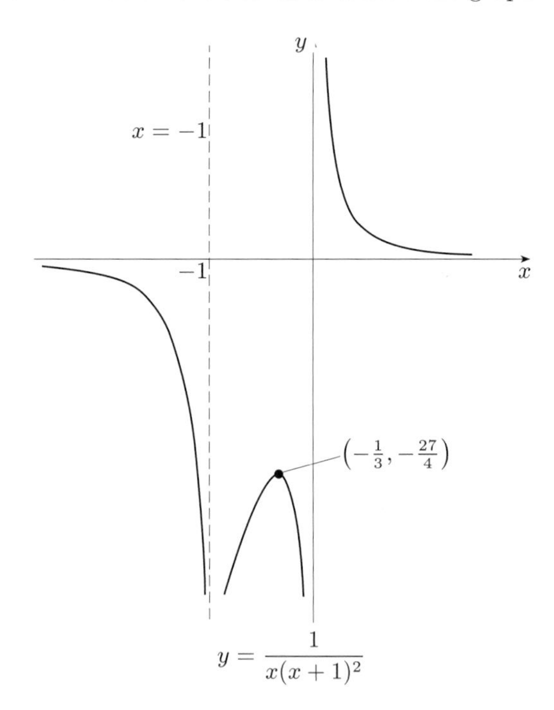

2.8 $f(x) = \frac{1}{5}x^5 - x^3$.

1. The domain of f is $\mathbb{R}$.

2. f is odd, since, for all x in $\mathbb{R}$,
$$f(-x) = \tfrac{1}{5}(-x)^5 - (-x)^3 = -(\tfrac{1}{5}x^5 - x^3) = -f(x).$$

3. $f(x) = \frac{1}{5}x^5 - x^3 = x^3(\frac{1}{5}x^2 - 1)$, so

$f(x) = 0$ when $x = 0$ and $x = \pm\sqrt{5}$.

So the x-intercepts are 0 and $\pm\sqrt{5}$, and the y-intercept is 0.

4. We construct a sign table for $f(x)$.

x		$-\sqrt{5}$	$(-\sqrt{5},0)$	0	$(0,\sqrt{5})$	$\sqrt{5}$	
x^3	$-$	$-$	$-$	0	$+$	$+$	$+$
$\frac{1}{5}x^2-1$	$+$	0	$-$	$-$	$-$	0	$+$
$f(x)$	$-$	0	$+$	0	$-$	0	$+$

Thus

f is positive on the intervals $(-\sqrt{5},0)$ and $(\sqrt{5},\infty)$;

f is negative on the intervals $(-\infty,-\sqrt{5})$ and $(0,\sqrt{5})$.

5. $f'(x)=x^4-3x^2=x^2(x^2-3)$, so

$f'(x)=0$ when $x=0$ and $\pm\sqrt{3}$;

$f'(x)>0$ when $x^2>3$;

$f'(x)<0$ when $x^2<3$.

Thus

f is increasing on the intervals $(-\infty,-\sqrt{3})$ and $(\sqrt{3},\infty)$;

f is decreasing on the intervals $(-\sqrt{3},0)$ and $(0,\sqrt{3})$;

f has stationary points at $x=-\sqrt{3}$, 0 and $\sqrt{3}$.

We deduce that

there is a local maximum at $x=-\sqrt{3}$ with $f(-\sqrt{3})=\frac{6}{5}\sqrt{3}$;

there is a local minimum at $x=\sqrt{3}$; with $f(\sqrt{3})=-\frac{6}{5}\sqrt{3}$;

there is a horizontal point of inflection at $x=0$.

6. The polynomial has degree 5 (odd), and the coefficient of x^5 is positive, so

$f(x)\to\infty$ as $x\to\infty$,

$f(x)\to-\infty$ as $x\to-\infty$.

This information enables us to sketch the graph.

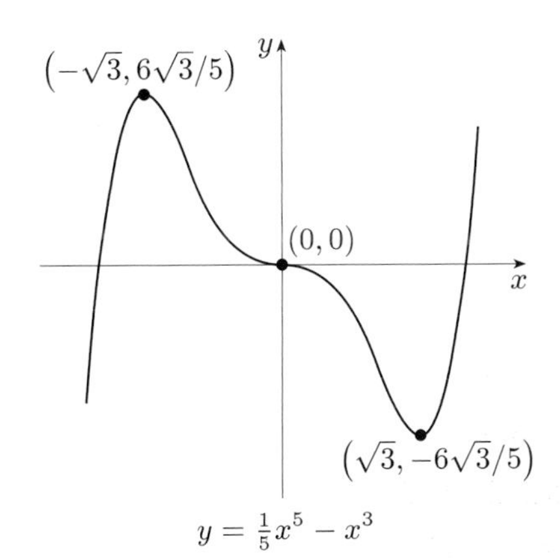

2.9 $f(x)=\dfrac{4x+3}{x-7}$.

1. The domain of f is $\mathbb{R}$, excluding 7.

2. f is neither even nor odd, since its domain is not symmetric about the origin.

3. $f(x)=0$ when $x=-\frac{3}{4}$, so the x-intercept is $-\frac{3}{4}$. The y-intercept is $f(0)=-\frac{3}{7}$.

4. We construct a sign table for $f(x)$.

x	$(-\infty,-\frac{3}{4})$	$-\frac{3}{4}$	$(-\frac{3}{4},7)$	7	$(7,\infty)$
$4x+3$	$-$	0	$+$	$+$	$+$
$x-7$	$-$	$-$	$-$	0	$+$
$f(x)$	$+$	0	$-$	$*$	$+$

Thus

f is positive on the intervals $(-\infty,-\frac{3}{4})$ and $(7,\infty)$;

f is negative on the interval $(-\frac{3}{4},7)$.

5. $f'(x)=\dfrac{(x-7)4-(4x+3)}{(x-7)^2}=\dfrac{-31}{(x-7)^2}$,

so $f'(x)<0$ for all x in the domain.

Thus f is decreasing on each interval of its domain.

6. The denominator is 0 when $x=7$, so

the line $x=7$ is a vertical asymptote.

Also, from step 4,

$f(x)\to-\infty$ as $x\to 7^-$,

$f(x)\to\infty$ as $x\to 7^+$.

Dividing both numerator and denominator of $f(x)$ by x, we obtain

$$f(x)=\frac{4+3/x}{1-7/x}\to 4 \quad \text{as } x\to\pm\infty,$$

so

the line $y=4$ is a horizontal asymptote.

This information enables us to sketch the graph.

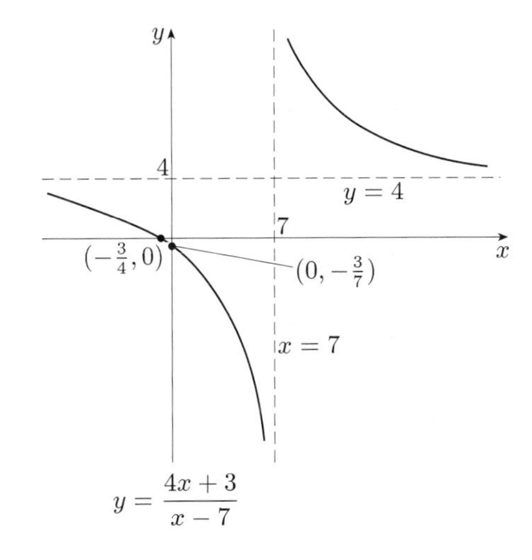

2.10 $f(x)=\dfrac{2x}{x^2+x-2}$.

1. We factorise $f(x)$ as follows:

$$f(x)=\frac{2x}{(x-1)(x+2)}.$$

Thus the domain of f is $\mathbb{R}$, excluding 1 and -2; it consists of the intervals $(-\infty,-2)$, $(-2,1)$ and $(1,\infty)$.

2. f is neither even nor odd, since its domain is not symmetric about the origin.

3. $f(x) = 0$ when $x = 0$, so 0 is both the x-intercept and the y-intercept.

4. We construct a sign table for $f(x)$.

x	$(-\infty, -2)$	-2	$(-2, 0)$	0	$(0, 1)$	1	$(1, \infty)$
$2x$	$-$	$-$	$-$	0	$+$	$+$	$+$
$x - 1$	$-$	$-$	$-$	$-$	$-$	0	$+$
$x + 2$	$-$	0	$+$	$+$	$+$	$+$	$+$
$f(x)$	$-$	*	$+$	0	$-$	*	$+$

Thus

f is positive on the intervals $(-2, 0)$ and $(1, \infty)$;

f is negative on the intervals $(-\infty, -2)$ and $(0, 1)$.

5. $$f'(x) = \frac{(x^2 + x - 2)2 - 2x(2x + 1)}{(x^2 + x - 2)^2} = \frac{-2x^2 - 4}{(x^2 + x - 2)^2} = \frac{-2(x^2 + 2)}{(x^2 + x - 2)^2},$$
so $f'(x) < 0$ for all x in the domain. Thus f is decreasing on each interval of its domain.

6. The denominator is 0 when $x = 1$ and $x = -2$, so

the lines $x = -2$ and $x = 1$ are vertical asymptotes.

Also, from step 4,

$$f(x) \to -\infty \quad \text{as } x \to -2^-,$$
$$f(x) \to \infty \quad \text{as } x \to -2^+,$$
$$f(x) \to -\infty \quad \text{as } x \to 1^-,$$
$$f(x) \to \infty \quad \text{as } x \to 1^+.$$

Dividing both numerator and denominator of $f(x)$ by the dominant term of the denominator, x^2, we obtain

$$f(x) = \frac{2/x}{1 + 1/x - 2/x^2} \to 0 \quad \text{as } x \to \pm\infty,$$

so

the line $y = 0$ is a horizontal asymptote.

This information enables us to sketch the graph.

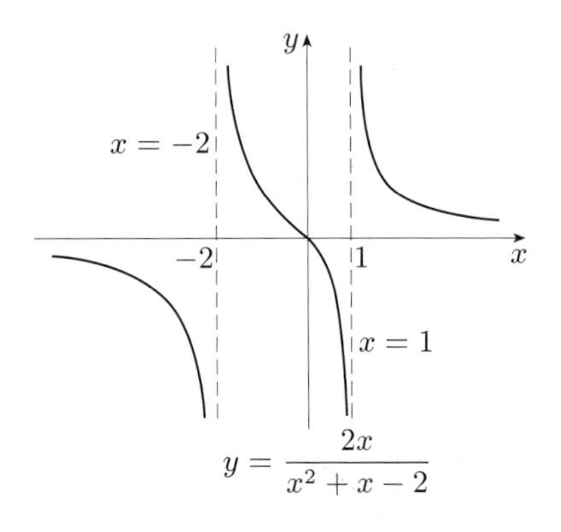

2.11 $f(x) = \dfrac{1}{\sqrt{1 + x^2}}$.

1. The domain of f is $\mathbb{R}$.

2. f is even, since, for all x in $\mathbb{R}$,
$$f(-x) = \frac{1}{\sqrt{1 + (-x)^2}} = \frac{1}{\sqrt{1 + x^2}} = f(x).$$

3. $f(x) = 0$ has no solution, so there are no x-intercepts.
The y-intercept is $f(0) = 1$.

4. f is positive on $\mathbb{R}$.

5. f is decreasing on the interval $(0, \infty)$;
f is increasing on the interval $(-\infty, 0)$.
We deduce that there is a local maximum at $x = 0$ with $f(0) = 1$.

6. $f(x) \to 0$ as $x \to \pm\infty$, so

the line $y = 0$ is a horizontal asymptote.

In order to obtain more information about the shape of the curve, we could find another point on the graph, for example $f(1) = 1/\sqrt{2} = \sqrt{2}/2 \simeq 0.707$.
This information enables us to sketch the graph.

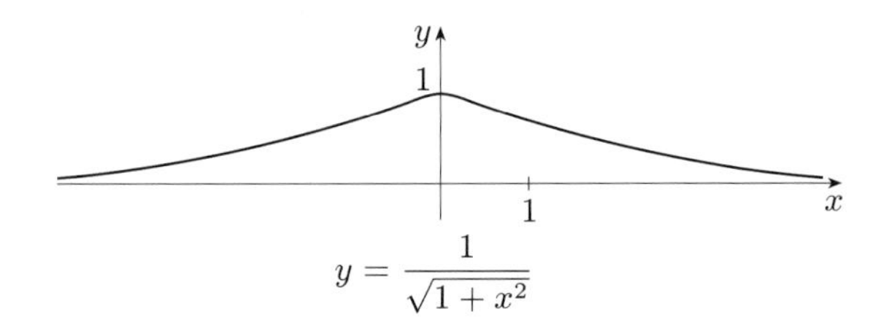

3.1 $f(x) = x \cos x$.

1. The function f has domain $\mathbb{R}$.

2. The function f is odd, since
$-x\cos(-x) = -x\cos x$ for all x in $\mathbb{R}$.
It is therefore sufficient initially to consider the features of $f(x)$ only for $x \geq 0$, and then to rotate the graph we obtain about the origin.

3. $f(x) = 0$ when $x = 0$ and when $\cos x = 0$; that is, when $x = 0, \pi/2, 3\pi/2, \ldots$. So the x-intercepts are $0, \pi/2, 3\pi/2, \ldots$ and the y-intercept is 0.

4. For $x > 0$, the intervals on which f is positive or negative alternate between the zeros in the same way as for the cosine function. That is,
f is positive on
$(0, \pi/2), (3\pi/2, 5\pi/2), (7\pi/2, 9\pi/2), \ldots$,
f is negative on
$(\pi/2, 3\pi/2), (5\pi/2, 7\pi/2), \ldots$.

5. $f'(x) = \cos x - x \sin x$, so we omit solving $f'(x) = 0$, as it is not easy.

6. The function has no asymptotes.

7. $-1 \leq \cos x \leq 1$ for all real numbers x, so we have
$$-x \leq x\cos x \leq x \quad \text{for } x > 0,$$
$$-x \geq x\cos x \geq x \quad \text{for } x < 0.$$

These inequalities tell us that

$$-|x| \le f(x) \le |x|, \quad \text{for all real numbers } x,$$

so the graph of f lies between the graphs of the functions $x \longmapsto |x|$ and $x \longmapsto -|x|$. These graphs are the construction lines for this function.

This information enables us to sketch the graph.

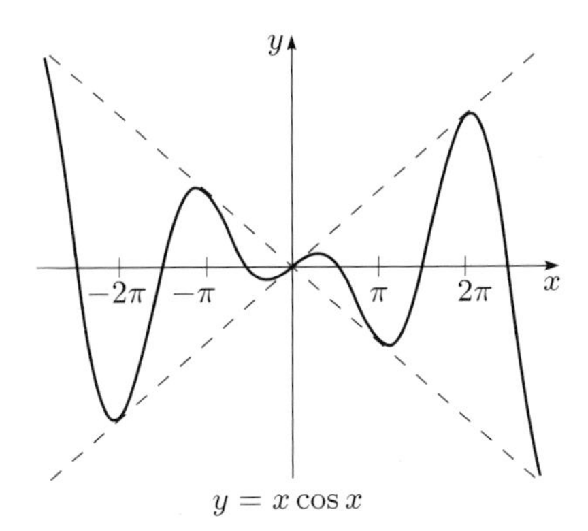

$y = x\cos x$

3.2 $f(x) = x + \sin x$

1. The function f has domain $\mathbb{R}$, since both x and $\sin x$ have domain $\mathbb{R}$.

2. $x + \sin x$ is odd, since for all x in $\mathbb{R}$,

$$-x + \sin(-x) = -(x + \sin x).$$

3. $f(0) = 0$, so 0 is both the x-intercept and the y-intercept. There are no other values of x for which $f(x) = 0$.

4. $f(x) > 0$ when $x > 0$. Since f is odd, then f is negative for $x < 0$.

5. $f'(x) = 1 + \cos x$, so $f'(x) = 0$ when $\cos x = -1$, that is, when $x = (2k+1)\pi$, for any integer k. At all other points in $\mathbb{R}$, $f'(x) > 0$, so f is increasing on $\mathbb{R}$. It has stationary points where $x = (2k+1)\pi$, but since f is increasing on $\mathbb{R}$ they are neither maxima nor minima, but are horizontal points of inflection.

6. The function has no asymptotes.

7. $-1 \le \sin x \le 1$, for all x in $\mathbb{R}$, so

$$x - 1 \le x + \sin x \le x + 1, \quad \text{for all } x \text{ in } \mathbb{R}.$$

So the graph of f lies between the lines $y = x - 1$ and $y = x + 1$.

Also, for all integers k,

when $x = k\pi$, $\sin x = 0$,

so $f(x) = x$;

when $x = (2k + \frac{1}{2})\pi$, $\sin x = 1$,

so $f(x) = x + 1$;

when $x = (2k + \frac{3}{2})\pi$, $\sin x = -1$,

so $f(x) = x - 1$.

So $y = x - 1$, $y = x + 1$ and $y = x$ can be used as construction lines.

This information enables us to sketch the graph.

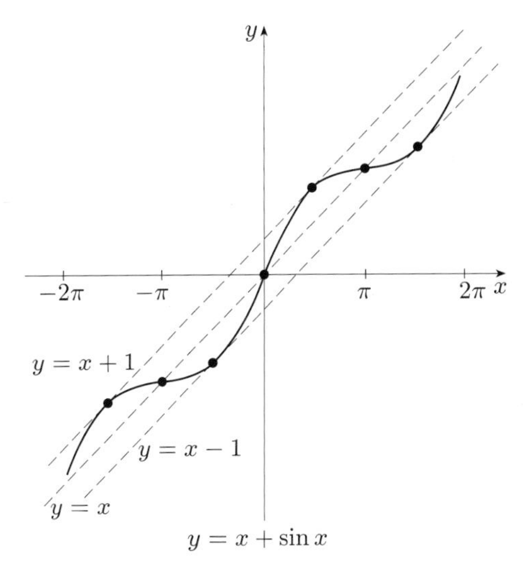

$y = x + \sin x$

3.3 Here it is sufficient to notice that the modulus function maps any negative value of $\sin x$ to the corresponding positive value. We therefore obtain the following graph.

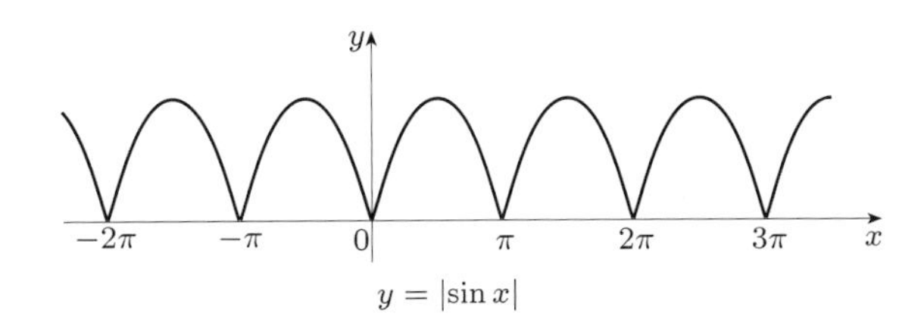

$y = |\sin x|$

There are local maxima with value 1 at $x = \frac{1}{2}(2k+1)\pi$, for any integer k;

there are local minima with value 0 at $x = k\pi$, for any integer k.

3.4

(a)

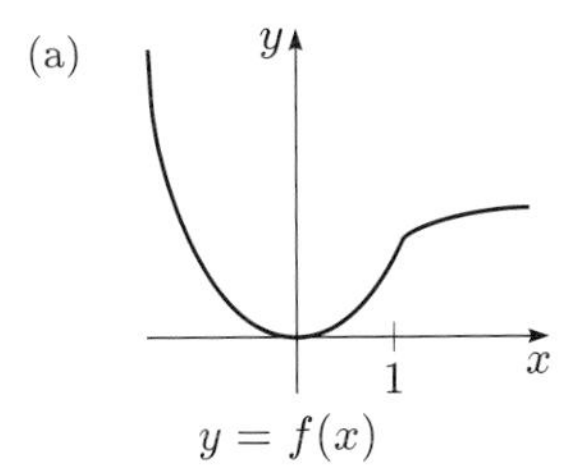

$y = f(x)$

(b)

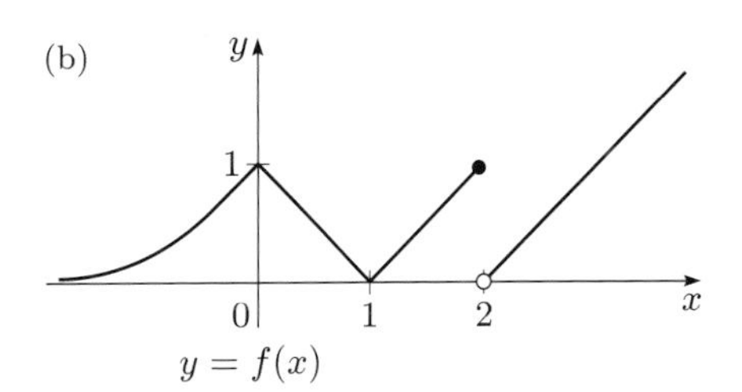

$y = f(x)$

(c)

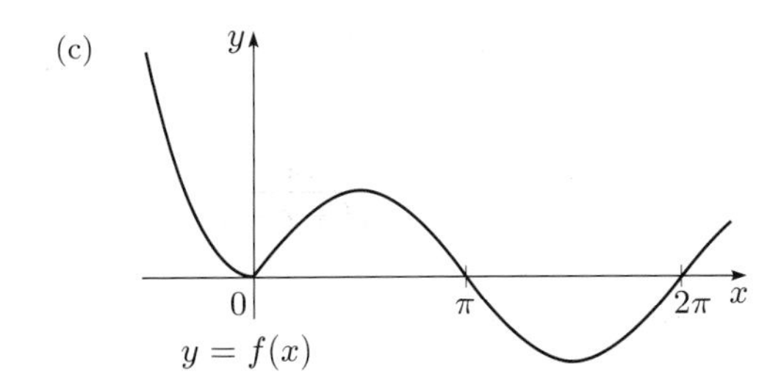

$y = f(x)$

3.5 $f(x) = 2\cos x - x$.

1. The domain of f is $\mathbb{R}$.

2. f is not even, odd or periodic.

3. $f(x) = 0$ is not easy to solve, but we know that $f(0) = 2$, which is positive, and $f(\pi/2) = -\pi/2$, which is negative, so there is an x-intercept in the interval $(0, \pi/2)$.

The y-intercept is 2.

4. Since there is only one x-intercept, f is positive when x is less than its value at the intercept, and negative when x is greater than its value at the intercept.

5. $f'(x) = -2\sin x - 1$, so $f'(x) = 0$ when $\sin x = -\frac{1}{2}$; that is, when $x = -\pi/6 + 2k\pi$ or $x = -5\pi/6 + 2k\pi$, for any integer k.

6. The function has no asymptotes.

7. Since

$$-2 \le 2\cos x \le 2, \quad \text{for all } x \text{ in } \mathbb{R},$$

then

$$-2 - x \le 2\cos x - x \le 2 - x, \quad \text{for all } x \text{ in } \mathbb{R}.$$

Therefore the graph of f lies between the construction lines $y = -2 - x$ and $y = 2 - x$.

Also, for any integer k,

when $x = 2k\pi$, $\cos 2k\pi = 1$,
so $f(x) = 2 - x$;

when $x = (2k+1)\pi$, $\cos(2k+1)\pi = -1$,
so $f(x) = -2 - x$;

when $x = (k + \frac{1}{2})\pi$, $\cos(k + \frac{1}{2})\pi = 0$,
so $f(x) = -x$.

Thus we obtain the following graph.

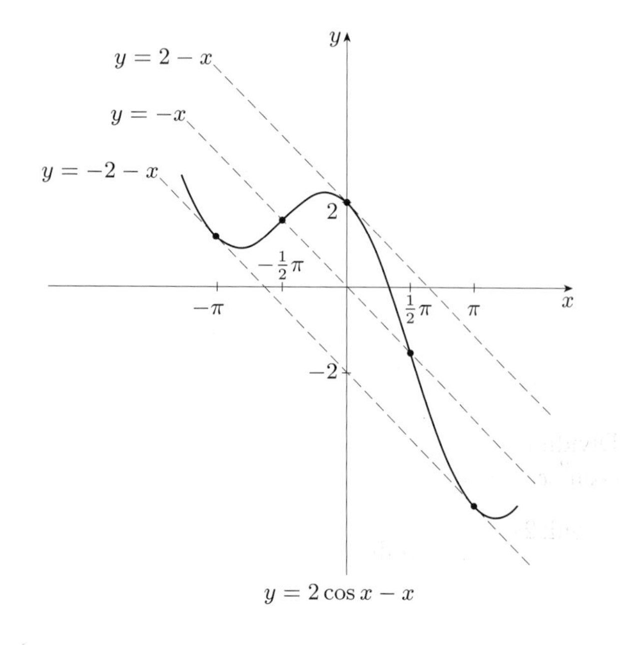

3.6 $f(x) = \dfrac{\cos x}{x}$.

1. The domain of f is $\mathbb{R}$, excluding 0.

2. f is odd, since, for all x in the domain,

$$f(-x) = \frac{\cos(-x)}{-x} = \frac{\cos x}{-x} = -\frac{\cos x}{x} = -f(x).$$

3. $f(x) = 0$ whenever $\cos x = 0$; that is, $f(x) = 0$ when $x = (k + \frac{1}{2})\pi$, for any integer k. $f(0)$ is not defined, so there is no y-intercept.

5. The equation $f'(x) = 0$ is not easy to solve, so we omit it.

6. The denominator is 0 when $x = 0$, so

the line $x = 0$ is a vertical asymptote,

and

$$f(x) \to \infty \quad \text{as } x \to 0^+,$$
$$f(x) \to -\infty \quad \text{as } x \to 0^-.$$

7. We know that $-1 \le \cos x \le 1$ for all x in $\mathbb{R}$.

For $x > 0$, we have $\dfrac{1}{x} > 0$, so

$$-\frac{1}{x} \le \frac{\cos x}{x} \le \frac{1}{x};$$

and for $x < 0$, we have $\dfrac{1}{x} < 0$, so

$$-\frac{1}{x} \ge \frac{\cos x}{x} \ge \frac{1}{x}.$$

Hence

$$-\left|\frac{1}{x}\right| \le \frac{\cos x}{x} \le \left|\frac{1}{x}\right|, \quad \text{for all non-zero } x \text{ in } \mathbb{R}.$$

So the graph of f lies between the graphs $y = -|1/x|$ and $y = |1/x|$, the construction lines, and meets these graphs when $\cos x = \pm 1$.

Thus we obtain the following graph.

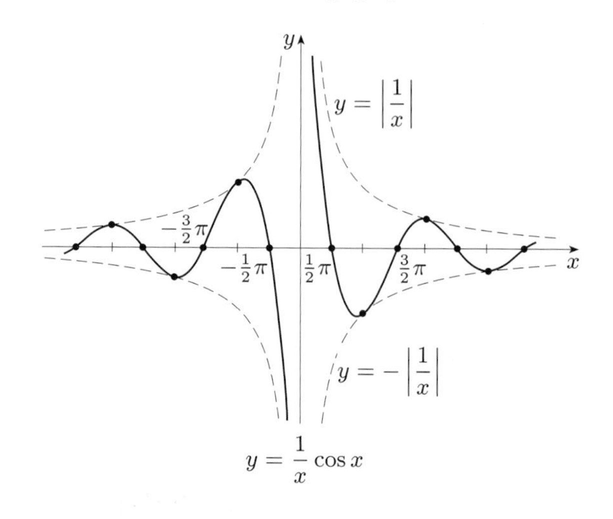

3.7

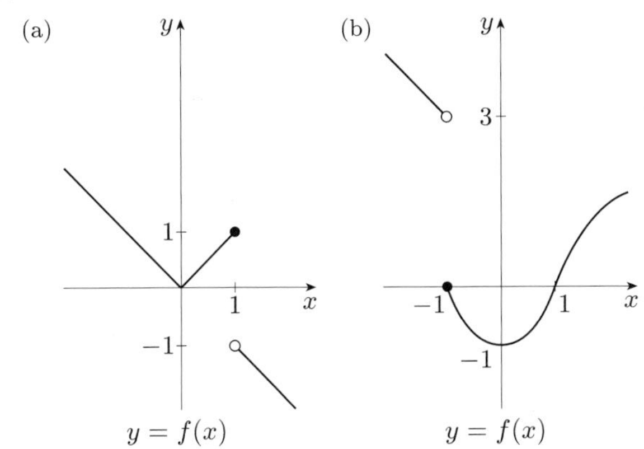

4.1 (a) $e^x(e^x + e^{-x}) = e^{2x} + e^x e^{-x} = e^{2x} + 1$

(b) $(e^{2x} - e^{-2x})/e^x = e^x - e^{-3x}$

(c) $(e^{5x} + e^{-5x})(e^{5x} - e^{-5x})$
$= e^{10x} - e^{5x}e^{-5x} + e^{-5x}e^{5x} - e^{-10x}$
$= e^{10x} - 1 + 1 - e^{-10x}$
$= e^{10x} - e^{-10x}$

4.2 (a) $\cosh^2 x - \sinh^2 x$
$= \frac{1}{4}(e^x + e^{-x})^2 - \frac{1}{4}(e^x - e^{-x})^2$
$= \frac{1}{4}((e^{2x} + 2e^x e^{-x} + e^{-2x}) - (e^{2x} - 2e^x e^{-x} + e^{-2x}))$
$= \frac{1}{4}(e^{2x} + 2 + e^{-2x} - e^{2x} + 2 - e^{-2x})$
$= \frac{1}{4} \times 4 = 1$

(b) $\cosh x \cosh y + \sinh x \sinh y$
$= \frac{1}{2}(e^x + e^{-x})\frac{1}{2}(e^y + e^{-y})$
$+ \frac{1}{2}(e^x - e^{-x})\frac{1}{2}(e^y - e^{-y})$
$= \frac{1}{4}(e^x e^y + e^x e^{-y} + e^{-x}e^y + e^{-x}e^{-y})$
$+ \frac{1}{4}(e^x e^y - e^x e^{-y} - e^{-x}e^y + e^{-x}e^{-y})$
$= \frac{1}{4}(e^{x+y} + e^{x-y} + e^{-x+y} + e^{-(x+y)})$
$+ \frac{1}{4}(e^{x+y} - e^{x-y} - e^{-x+y} + e^{-(x+y)})$
$= \frac{1}{2}(e^{x+y} + e^{-(x+y)})$
$= \cosh(x+y)$

(c) $\sinh x \cosh y + \cosh x \sinh y$
$= \frac{1}{2}(e^x - e^{-x})\frac{1}{2}(e^y + e^{-y})$
$+ \frac{1}{2}(e^x + e^{-x})\frac{1}{2}(e^y - e^{-y})$
$= \frac{1}{4}(e^x e^y + e^x e^{-y} - e^{-x}e^y - e^{-x}e^{-y})$
$+ \frac{1}{4}(e^x e^y - e^x e^{-y} + e^{-x}e^y - e^{-x}e^{-y})$
$= \frac{1}{4}(e^{x+y} + e^{x-y} - e^{-x+y} - e^{-(x+y)})$
$+ \frac{1}{4}(e^{x+y} - e^{x-y} + e^{-x+y} - e^{-(x+y)})$
$= \frac{1}{2}(e^{x+y} - e^{-(x+y)})$
$= \sinh(x+y)$

4.3 Let $f(x) = \cosh x = \frac{1}{2}(e^x + e^{-x})$; then

$$f'(x) = \tfrac{1}{2}(e^x - e^{-x}) = \sinh x.$$

Let $g(x) = \sinh x = \frac{1}{2}(e^x - e^{-x})$; then

$$g'(x) = \tfrac{1}{2}(e^x + e^{-x}) = \cosh x.$$

Thus

$$\cosh' = \sinh \quad \text{and} \quad \sinh' = \cosh.$$

These are similar to the trigonometric derivatives

$$\cos' = -\sin \quad \text{and} \quad \sin' = \cos,$$

but differ by a minus sign in the first one.

4.4 (a) $f(-x) = \tanh(-x)$
$$= \frac{e^{-x} - e^x}{e^{-x} + e^x} = -\left(\frac{e^x - e^{-x}}{e^x + e^{-x}}\right) = -\tanh x = -f(x),$$

so tanh is an odd function.

(b) $f(x) = \tanh x = \dfrac{e^x - e^{-x}}{e^x + e^{-x}}$.

Dividing both numerator and denominator by e^x (non-zero for all x in $\mathbb{R}$), we obtain

$$f(x) = \frac{1 - e^{-2x}}{1 + e^{-2x}}.$$

(c) $f(x) = \tanh x = \dfrac{\sinh x}{\cosh x}$.

Differentiating the quotient, we obtain

$$f'(x) = \frac{\cosh x(\cosh x) - \sinh x(\sinh x)}{\cosh^2 x},$$

and using the result from Exercise 4.2(a), we obtain

$$f'(x) = \frac{\cosh^2 x - \sinh^2 x}{\cosh^2 x} = \frac{1}{\cosh^2 x} = \operatorname{sech}^2 x.$$

Since $\operatorname{sech}^2 x$ is positive for all x in $\mathbb{R}$, it follows that

$$f'(x) > 0, \quad \text{for all } x \text{ in } \mathbb{R}.$$

4.5 (a) Since $\cosh 2x = \cosh^2 x + \sinh^2 x$ and $\cosh^2 x - \sinh^2 x = 1$, we have

$$\cosh 2x = \frac{\cosh^2 x + \sinh^2 x}{\cosh^2 x - \sinh^2 x}.$$

Dividing both numerator and denominator by $\cosh^2 x$ (which is never 0), we obtain

$$\cosh 2x = \frac{1 + \tanh^2 x}{1 - \tanh^2 x}.$$

(b) Since $\sinh 2x = 2 \sinh x \cosh x$ and $\cosh^2 x - \sinh^2 x = 1$, we obtain

$$\sinh 2x = \frac{2 \sinh x \cosh x}{\cosh^2 x - \sinh^2 x}.$$

Dividing both numerator and denominator by $\cosh^2 x$, we obtain

$$\sinh 2x = \frac{2 \tanh x}{1 - \tanh^2 x}.$$

4.6 $f(x) = \sinh x$.

1. $\sinh x$ has domain $\mathbb{R}$.

2. $\sinh x$ is odd, since

$$\begin{aligned}\sinh(-x) &= \tfrac{1}{2}(e^{-x} - e^{-(-x)})\\ &= \tfrac{1}{2}(e^{-x} - e^{x})\\ &= -\tfrac{1}{2}(e^{x} - e^{-x}) = -\sinh x.\end{aligned}$$

3. $\sinh x = \frac{1}{2}(e^x - e^{-x}) = 0$ when $e^x = e^{-x}$; so the only zero of $\sinh x$ is 0. So 0 is both the x-intercept and the y-intercept.

4. From the graphs of $y = e^x$ and $y = e^{-x}$, we observe that

$$\sinh x > 0, \quad \text{for } x > 0,$$
$$\sinh x < 0, \quad \text{for } x < 0.$$

5. From Exercise 4.3, we know that

$$\sinh' x = \cosh x.$$

Also, we know that

$$\cosh x \geq 1, \quad \text{for all } x \text{ in } \mathbb{R},$$

so $\sinh x$ is strictly increasing on $\mathbb{R}$, and so has no local maxima or local minima.

Since $\sinh x' = \cosh x$ and $\cosh 0 = 1$, the graph of $\sinh x$ has slope 1 at the origin.

6. $e^x \to \infty$ as $x \to \infty$ and $e^{-x} \to 0$ as $x \to \infty$, so

$$f(x) \to \infty \quad \text{as } x \to \infty.$$

Since $\sinh x$ is an odd function,

$$f(x) \to -\infty \quad \text{as } x \to -\infty.$$

This information enables us to sketch the graph.

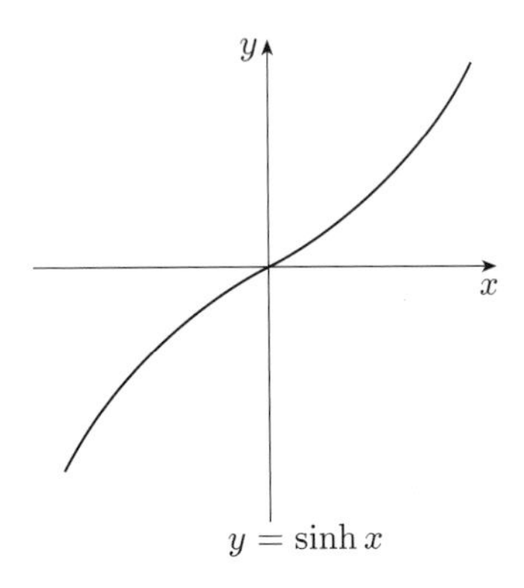

$y = \sinh x$

4.7 $f(x) = \tanh x = \dfrac{\sinh x}{\cosh x}$.

1. $\tanh x$ has domain $\mathbb{R}$, since $\cosh x$ never takes the value 0.

2. $\tanh x$ is odd, by Exercise 4.4(a).

3. $\cosh x \geq 1$ for all x in $\mathbb{R}$, so the zeros of $\tanh x$ are the same as those of $\sinh x$, namely 0. So 0 is both the x-intercept and the y-intercept.

4. $\tanh x$ is positive where $\sinh x$ is positive, namely on $(0, \infty)$;

$\tanh x$ is negative where $\sinh x$ is negative, namely on $(-\infty, 0)$.

5. We know, from Exercise 4.4(c), that $f'(x) > 0$ for all x in $\mathbb{R}$, so there are no local maxima or local minima.

Since $f'(0) = \operatorname{sech}^2(0) = 1$, the graph of $\tanh x$ has slope 1 at the origin.

6. Since $\cosh x \geq 1$, the denominator is never zero, so there are no vertical asymptotes.

Since $\tanh x = \dfrac{1 - e^{-2x}}{1 + e^{-2x}}$ (from Exercise 4.4(b)), and since $e^{-2x} \to 0$ as $x \to \infty$, we have $\tanh x \to \dfrac{1-0}{1+0}$ as $x \to \infty$, Since

$$\tanh x \to 1 \quad \text{as } x \to \infty.$$

Since tanh is an odd function,

$$\tanh x \to -1 \quad \text{as } x \to -\infty.$$

Thus

the lines $y = 1$ and $y = -1$

are horizontal asymptotes.

This information enables us to sketch the graph.

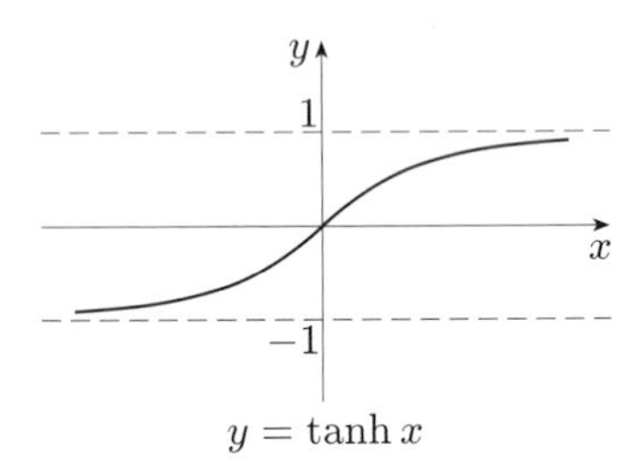

$y = \tanh x$

4.8 $\operatorname{cosech} x = \dfrac{1}{\sinh x}$.

1. $\sinh x = 0$ when $x = 0$, so $\operatorname{cosech} x$ is not defined at 0. Thus $\operatorname{cosech} x$ has domain $\mathbb{R}$, excluding 0.

2. $\operatorname{cosech} x$ is odd, since $\sinh x$ is odd.

3. and 4.

We know that

$$\sinh x > 0, \quad \text{for } x > 0,$$
$$\sinh x < 0, \quad \text{for } x < 0,$$

so

$$\operatorname{cosech} x > 0, \quad \text{for } x > 0,$$
$$\operatorname{cosech} x < 0, \quad \text{for } x < 0,$$

thus

$\operatorname{cosech} x$ has no zeros.

Also $\operatorname{cosech} x$ is not defined at $x = 0$, so $\operatorname{cosech} x$ has neither x-intercepts nor y-intercepts.

5. $\sinh x$ is increasing on $\mathbb{R}$, so $\operatorname{cosech} x$ is decreasing on the intervals $(-\infty, 0)$ and $(0, \infty)$, and thus has no local maxima or local minima.

6. The graph of $y = \sinh x$ indicates that:

when $x = 0$, $\sinh x = 0$;

$\sinh x \to \infty$ as $x \to \infty$;

$\sinh x \to -\infty$ as $x \to -\infty$.

But $\operatorname{cosech} x = 1/\sinh x$, and $\sinh x$ is small when x is close to 0, so

the line $x = 0$ is a vertical asymptote.

From steps 3 and 4,

$$\operatorname{cosech} x \to \infty \quad \text{as } x \to 0^+,$$
$$\operatorname{cosech} x \to -\infty \quad \text{as } x \to 0^-.$$

Also,

$$\operatorname{cosech} x \to 0 \quad \text{as } x \to \pm\infty.$$

This information enables us to sketch the graph.

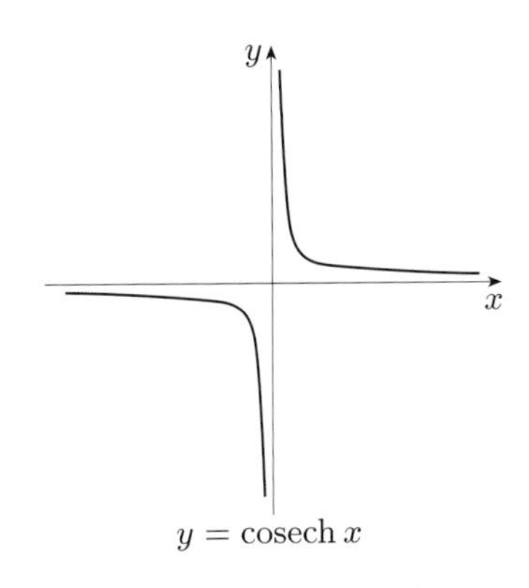

4.9 $$\tanh(x+y) = \frac{\sinh(x+y)}{\cosh(x+y)} = \frac{\sinh x \cosh y + \cosh x \sinh y}{\cosh x \cosh y + \sinh x \sinh y}.$$

Dividing both numerator and denominator by $\cosh x \cosh y$, we obtain

$$\tanh(x+y) = \frac{\dfrac{\sinh x}{\cosh x} + \dfrac{\sinh y}{\cosh y}}{1 + \dfrac{\sinh x \sinh y}{\cosh x \cosh y}} = \frac{\tanh x + \tanh y}{1 + \tanh x \tanh y}.$$

4.10 See Exercise 4.7 for the graph of $\tanh x$.
$f(x) = \coth x = 1/\tanh x$.

1. $\tanh x = 0$ when $x = 0$, so the domain of $\coth x$ is the set of all real numbers, excluding 0.
2. $\tanh x$ is odd, so $\coth x$ is odd.
3. $\coth x$ has neither x- nor y-intercepts.
4. We know that

$$\tanh x > 0 \quad \text{when } x > 0,$$
$$\tanh x < 0 \quad \text{when } x < 0,$$

so

$$\coth x > 0 \quad \text{when } x > 0,$$
$$\coth x < 0 \quad \text{when } x < 0.$$

5. $\tanh x$ is increasing on $\mathbb{R}$, so $\coth x$ is decreasing on each interval of its domain, and so has no local maxima or minima.
6. $\tanh x \to 1$ as $x \to \infty$, so

$$\coth x \to 1 \quad \text{as } x \to \infty;$$

$\tanh x \to -1$ as $x \to -\infty$, so

$$\coth x \to -1 \quad \text{as } x \to -\infty.$$

$\tanh x$ is small when x is close to 0, so

the line $x = 0$ is a vertical asymptote.

Also,

$$\coth x \to \infty \quad \text{as } x \to 0^+,$$
$$\coth x \to -\infty \quad \text{as } x \to 0^-.$$

Thus we obtain the following graph.

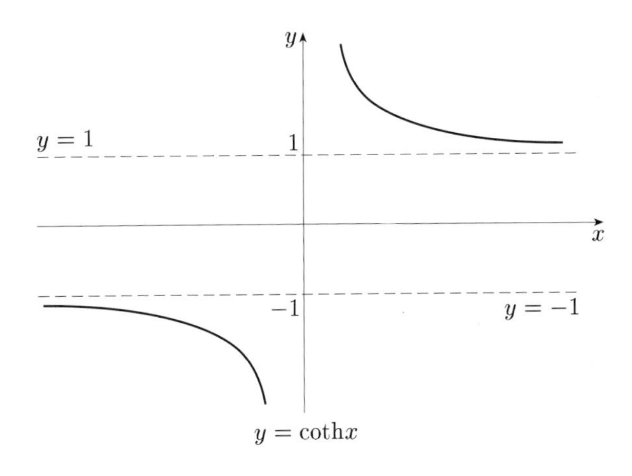

5.1 We have

$$x = t - \sin t, \quad y = 1 - \cos t.$$

When $t = \pi/3$,

$$x = \frac{\pi}{3} - \frac{\sqrt{3}}{2} \simeq 1.047 - 0.866 = 0.181,$$
$$y = 1 - \frac{1}{2} = 0.5.$$

When $t = \pi$,

$$x = \pi - 0 \simeq 3.142,$$
$$y = 1 - (-1) = 2.$$

When $t = \pi/2$,

$$x = \pi/2 - 1 \simeq 1.571 - 1 = 0.571,$$
$$y = 1 - 0 = 1.$$

When $t = \pi/6$,

$$x = \frac{\pi}{6} - \frac{1}{2} \simeq 0.524 - 0.5 = 0.024,$$
$$y = 1 - \frac{\sqrt{3}}{2} \simeq 1 - 0.866 = 0.134.$$

5.2

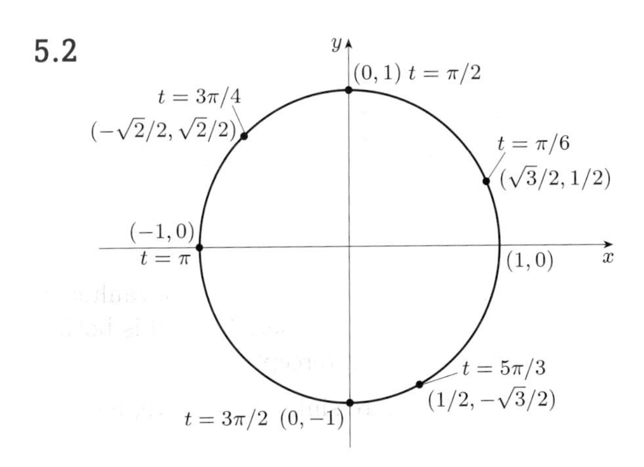

5.3 (a) $\alpha(t) = (3\cos t, 3\sin t)$, for t in $[0, 2\pi]$.

(b) $\alpha(t) = (2 + 3\cos t, 1 + 3\sin t)$, for t in $[0, 2\pi]$.

5.4 Let $x = \cos 2\pi t$, $y = \sin 2\pi t$, for t in $[0, 1]$; then

$$x^2 + y^2 = \cos^2 2\pi t + \sin^2 2\pi t = 1,$$

so (x, y) is a point on the unit circle. As t increases from 0 to 1, $2\pi t$ increases from 0 to 2π, so the point (x, y) moves once round the circle.

5.5 (a) $\alpha(t) = (1 + 2t, 2 + 4t)$, for t in $\mathbb{R}$.

(b) $t = \frac{1}{2}$, $t = 3$, $t = -\frac{1}{2}$.

5.6 Eliminating t, we obtain

$$t^3 = \frac{x}{p},$$

so

$$y = qt^3 = \frac{q}{p}x,$$

which is the equation of the line through the points $(0, 0)$ and (p, q).

5.7 (a)

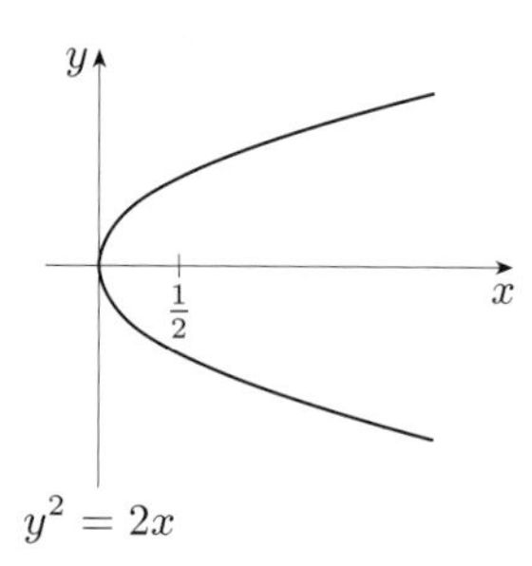

$y^2 = 2x$

$\alpha(t) = (\frac{1}{2}t^2, t)$, for t in $\mathbb{R}$.

(b)

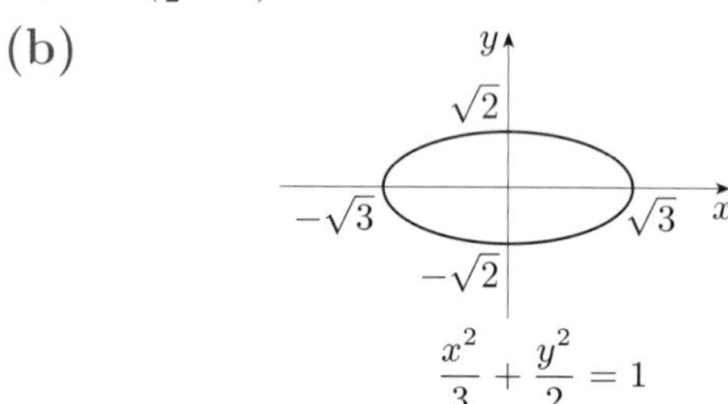

$$\frac{x^2}{3} + \frac{y^2}{2} = 1$$

$\alpha(t) = (\sqrt{3}\cos t, \sqrt{2}\sin t)$, for t in $[0, 2\pi]$.

(c)

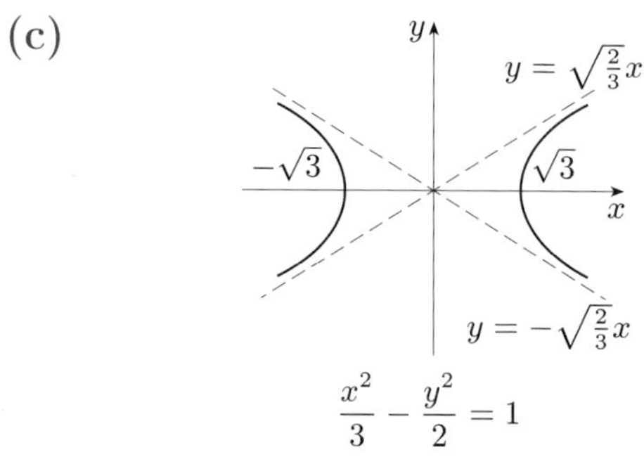

$$\frac{x^2}{3} - \frac{y^2}{2} = 1$$

$\alpha(t) = (\sqrt{3}\sec t, \sqrt{2}\tan t)$, for t in $[-\pi, \pi]$ excluding $-\pi/2$ and $\pi/2$.

5.8 The parametric equations for this curve are

$$x = a\cosh t, \quad y = b\sinh t.$$

We eliminate t by writing

$$x/a = \cosh t, \quad y/b = \sinh t$$

and using the identity

$$\cosh^2 t - \sinh^2 t = 1,$$

to obtain

$$\frac{x^2}{a^2} - \frac{y^2}{b^2} = 1,$$

the equation for a hyperbola in standard form.

Since $\cosh t$ is always positive, this parametrisation gives only *one* branch of the hyperbola, namely the branch corresponding to positive values of x (because $\cosh t$ takes all values in $[1, \infty)$). Since $\sinh t$ can be positive or negative, we get the *whole* of this branch.

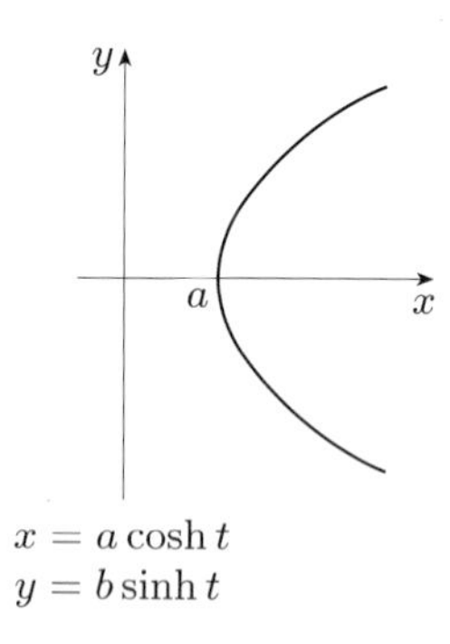

$x = a\cosh t$
$y = b\sinh t$

5.9 (a) $y = \dfrac{1}{x}$. Hence the curve is the graph of the reciprocal function.

(b) $t = x + 1$, so $y = 4 - 3(x + 1) = 1 - 3x$. Hence the curve is a straight line with slope -3 and y-intercept 1.

(c) $t = \dfrac{x}{2}$, so $y = 1 + 3\left(\dfrac{x}{2}\right)^2 = 1 + \dfrac{3x^2}{4}$.

Hence the curve is a parabola, symmetric about the y-axis, with vertex at $(0, 1)$.

5.10 (a)

$$\begin{aligned}
\alpha(0) &= (2(1) + 1, 2(0) + 0) = (3, 0)\\
\alpha(\tfrac{1}{6}\pi) &= (2(\tfrac{1}{2}\sqrt{3}) + \tfrac{1}{2}, 2(\tfrac{1}{2}) + \tfrac{1}{2}\sqrt{3})\\
&= (\sqrt{3} + \tfrac{1}{2}, 1 + \tfrac{1}{2}\sqrt{3}) \simeq (2.23, 1.87)\\
\alpha(\tfrac{1}{3}\pi) &= (2(\tfrac{1}{2}) + (-\tfrac{1}{2}), 2(\tfrac{1}{2}\sqrt{3}) + \tfrac{1}{2}\sqrt{3})\\
&= (\tfrac{1}{2}, \tfrac{3}{2}\sqrt{3}) \simeq (0.5, 2.60)\\
\alpha(\tfrac{1}{2}\pi) &= (2(0) - 1, 2(1) + 0) = (-1, 2)\\
\alpha(\tfrac{2}{3}\pi) &= (2(-\tfrac{1}{2}) + (-\tfrac{1}{2}), 2(\tfrac{1}{2}\sqrt{3}) + (-\tfrac{1}{2}\sqrt{3}))\\
&= (-\tfrac{3}{2}, \tfrac{1}{2}\sqrt{3}) \simeq (-1.5, 0.87)\\
\alpha(\tfrac{5}{6}\pi) &= (2(-\tfrac{1}{2}\sqrt{3}) + (\tfrac{1}{2}), 2(\tfrac{1}{2}) + (-\tfrac{1}{2}\sqrt{3}))\\
&= (-\sqrt{3} + \tfrac{1}{2}, 1 - \tfrac{1}{2}\sqrt{3}) \simeq (-1.23, 0.13)\\
\alpha(\pi) &= (2(-1) + 1, 2(0) + 0) = (-1, 0)
\end{aligned}$$

(b) $f(-t) = 2\cos(-t) + \cos(-2t)$
$= 2\cos t + \cos 2t$ (since cos is even)
$= f(t)$.

Hence f is even.

$g(-t) = 2\sin(-t) + \sin(-2t)$
$= -2\sin t - \sin 2t$ (since sin is odd)
$= -g(t)$.

Hence g is odd.

So we have

$$\alpha(t) = (f(t), g(t)) \quad \text{and} \quad \alpha(-t) = (f(t), -g(t)).$$

From this we deduce that the curve is symmetric about the x-axis.

(c) We plot the points obtained in part (a), and use part (b) to complete the curve—a *cardioid*.

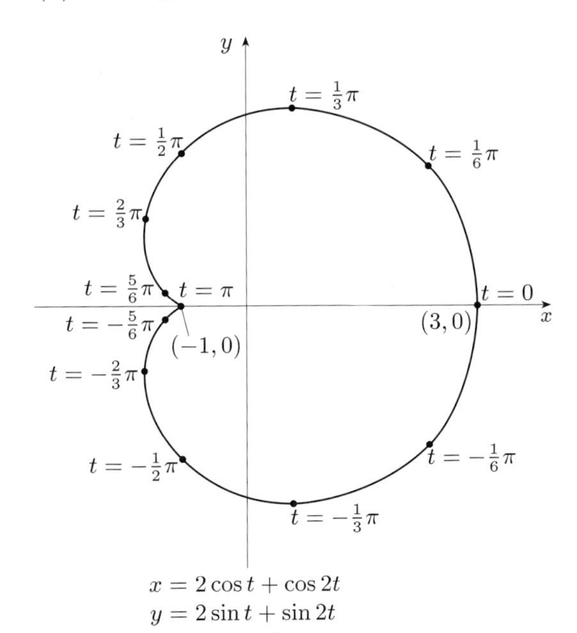

Index